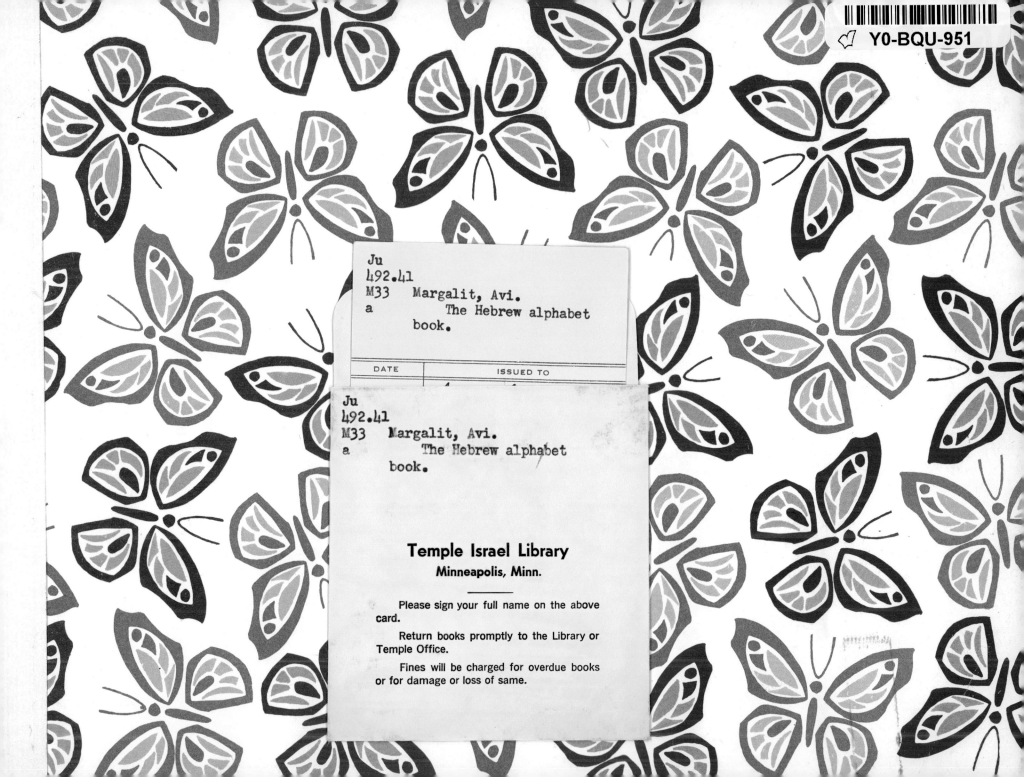

SURPRISE! SURPRISE!

The book you are now holding is a Hebrew book, or more correctly, a Hebrew and English book.

Hebrew is the language of the Bible. It is also one of the oldest languages in the world.

Practically nobody spoke Hebrew for nearly two thousand years, although many people read many ancient and holy books in Hebrew during that time.

In fact, when the United States was first in its infancy, and universities were just getting started, one of the first subjects that was taught was—Hebrew.

There are many interesting things about this ancient language which has once again become a popular and spoken language.

One of the strangest things for you to realize is that you are now at the back—yes, that's right, the back—of this book!

You see, Hebrew moves from right to left.

So, get ready, turn the book to the "back" and you'll be at the front—in Hebrew.

Have fun.

THE HEBREW ALPHABET BOOK

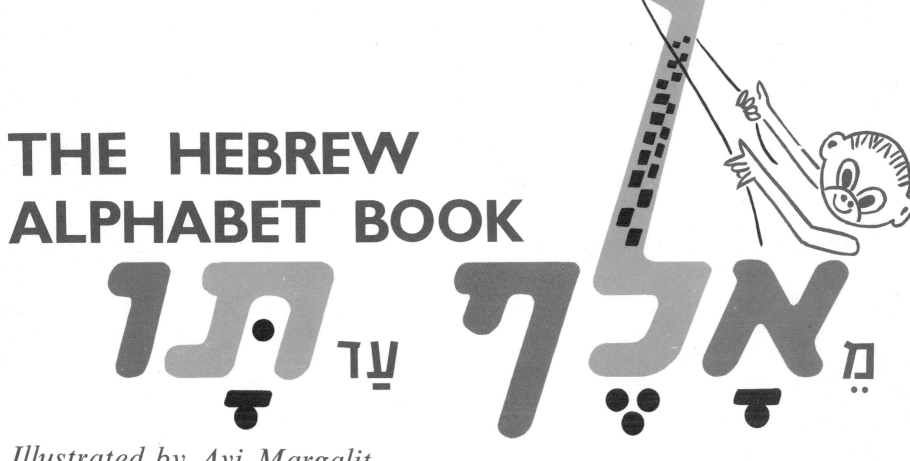

מֵאָלֶף עַד תָו

Illustrated by Avi Margalit

A SABRA BOOK · FUNK AND WAGNALLS · NEW YORK

For Rinat and Shuli, with love.
Abba, your father

© 1968 AMERICAN-ISRAEL PUBLISHING COMPANY, LTD.
LIBRARY OF CONGRESS CATALOG CARD NUMBER 68-55546
PRINTED IN ISRAEL

ת

TAV

תַּפּוּחַ

TAPUACH

Apple

תַּרְנְגוֹל

TARN'GOL

Rooster

שׁרקצפעסנמלכיטחזוהד

SHIN

שָׁפָן

SHAFAN

Rabbit

שֶׁמֶשׁ

SHEMESH

Sun

רֵישׁ

RESH

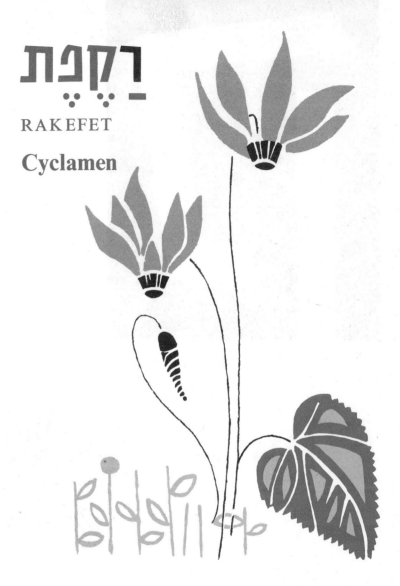

רַקֶּפֶת

RAKEFET

Cyclamen

רִמּוֹן

RIMON

Pomegranate

קוֹף

KOF

Monkey

קִפּוֹד

KIPOD

Porcupine

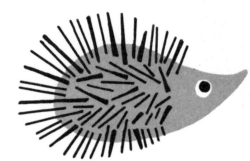

קן

אבגדהוזחט

TSADI

צִפּוֹר

TZIPOR

Bird

צָב

TZAV

Turtle

PAY

פִיל

PIL

Elephant

פַּרְפַּר

PARPAR

Butterfly

א ב ג ד ה

AYIN

עֵץ

ETZ

Tree

עַכְבָּר

ACHBAR

Mouse

SAMECH

סוּס

SOOS

Horse

סֵפֶל

SEFEL

Cup

NUN

נָמֵר

NAMER

Tiger

נַעֲלַיִם

NA'ALAYIM

Shoes

MEM

מַשְׁפֵּךְ

MASHPECH

Watering Can

מִסְפָּרַיִם

MISPARAYIM

Scissors

LAMED

LEITZAN

Clown

LIMON

Lemon

KAF

כֶּלֶב

KELEV

Dog

בִּסֵּא

KISAY

Chair

ו

YUD

יַלְדָּה

YALDA

Girl

יַנְשׁוּף

YANSHOOF

Owl

א ב ג ד ה ו ז ח ט י

TET

טְרַקְטוֹר

TRAKTOR

Tractor

טַוָּס

TAVAS

Peacock

ח HET

חָתוּל

HATUL

Cat

חֲסִידָה

HASSIDA

Stork

א ב ג ד ה ו ז ח

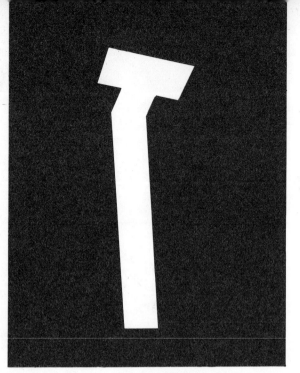

ZAYIN

זֵר

ZER

Wreath

זֶבְרָה

ZEBRA

Zebra

ו

VAV

וִילוֹן

VILON

Curtain

א ב ג ד ה ו

HEH

הָרִים

HARIM

Mountains

DALED

דָּג

DAG

Fish

דֻּבּוֹן

DUBON

Cub

GIMMEL

G'DI גְּדִי

Kid

GAMAL גָּמָל

Camel

BET

בַּיִת

BAYIT

House

בַּרְוָז

BARVAZ

Duck

ALEPH

אֲנִיָּה

ONI'YA

Ship

אַיָלָה

AYALA

Doe

VOL **6** DIA-ELE
439–526

FUNK & WAGNALLS **new**
ENCYCLOPEDIA
OF SCIENCE

FUNK & WAGNALLS, INC.

HOW TO USE FUNK & WAGNALLS NEW ENCYCLOPEDIA OF SCIENCE

Volumes 1 through 21 have information printed on the front covers, spine, and title pages that make it easy to find the articles you want to read.

- Volume numbers are printed in all three places in Volumes 1 through 21.
- Letter breaks — $\frac{COL}{DIA}$ — are printed in all three places in Volumes 1 through 21. The letters above the line are the first three letters of the first article title in the volume. The letters below the line are the first three letters of the last article title in the volume.
- Page breaks — $\frac{351}{438}$ — are printed on the spines and title pages of Volumes 1 through 21. They provide the page numbers of the first and last text pages in the volume.

Articles are arranged alphabetically by title in Volumes 1 through 21. Most titles are printed in **BOLD-FACE CAPITAL** letters. Some titles are printed in even larger letters.

- Some titles are not article titles, but refer you to the actual article title. Within articles you will find *See* or *See also* other article names for further information. All of these references to other articles are called cross-references.
- Most article titles are followed by a phonetic pronunciation. Use the Pronunciation Guide on page vi of Volume 1 to learn the correct pronunciation of the article title.
- At the end of most articles are two sets of initials. The first set identifies the person who wrote the article. The second set identifies the special consultant who checked the article for accuracy. All of these people are listed by their initials and full names and position on pages v and vi of Volume 1.
- ◤ This symbol at the end of an article indicates that there is a project based on the subject of the article in the Projects, Bibliography & Index volume. The project is found under its article title, and all of the project article titles are arranged alphabetically on pages 1 through 64 of the Projects, Bibliography & Index volume.

The Projects, Bibliography & Index Volume contains three sections. Each is an essential part of the encyclopedia.

- Projects based on articles in the encyclopedia are found in the first section. Each is both entertaining and educational. Each is designed for use by a student and for parental participation if desired.
- Bibliography reading lists in the second section list books under general scientific categories that are also titles of major articles. Each book listed is marked with either a YA (Young Adult) or J (Juvenile) reading level indicator. YA generally applies to readers at the junior high level or higher. J applies to readers at grade levels below junior high school.
- Index entries for all article titles plus many subjects that are not article titles are found in the third section. Instructions on using the Index are found at the start of the Index section in the Projects, Bibliography & Index volume.

DIAMOND

A diamond (dī′ mənd) is the hardest substance known that occurs in nature. It is also one of the most valuable and enduring (long-lasting) substances. Diamonds are a crystalline form of carbon. Diamond is closely related to the mineral graphite, which is also a form of carbon. Graphite, however, is a very soft substance. In graphite, the atoms of carbon are arranged in sheets that are stacked on top of one another. When graphite is treated with high pressure and temperature, the sheets of carbon atoms are broken up. The atoms are forced together into a much more tightly packed structure.

Scientists believe diamonds were formed underground millions of years ago from carbon that was subject to high temperature and pressure.

Diamonds may vary in color from white or nearly colorless to green, brown, yellow, pink, and sometimes black. The color is caused by impurities.

Where diamonds are found Diamonds are believed to have been first discovered in stream beds in India. India, however, produces few diamonds today. Russia supplies about 16% of the world's diamonds. Its deposits are in Siberia. South America, especially Brazil, is an important source of diamonds.

Almost 80% of the world's supply of

These photographs show a newly mined diamond (left), and a large uncut diamond, shown full size (right).

The Kimberley diamond mine (above) is in South Africa.

diamonds, however, comes from Africa. South Africa provides most of the high quality diamonds which are used for jewelry. Zaire, in Central Africa, is a main source of diamonds used in industry. In the United States, the only diamond mine is located in Arkansas.

The first diamonds, known as alluvial diamonds, were found in the sand and gravel of stream beds. Later, diamonds were found in rocks deep in the earth. The rock containing diamonds is called blue ground. Many tons of blue ground must be taken from deep in the earth, then crushed and sorted, to obtain one small diamond. Even in the richest deposits of South Africa, an average of only 1 carat (200 mg) of diamond is found for every 2.7 metric tons [3 tons] of blue ground mined.

Diamonds as gem stones Diamonds are able to reflect light, bend rays of light, and break up into all colors of the rainbow. To produce the greatest brilliance, many little sides, called facets, must be cut and polished on a diamond. Each tiny facet must be exactly the right size and shape, and placed exactly at the correct angle. A thin, circular saw that holds diamond dust is used to cut a rough diamond. Cutters use the lopping method to grind facets. Lopping involves carefully pressing the diamond against a rotating wheel coated with diamond dust. The style of cut often seen today is the round shape with 58 facets, known as the brilliant cut.

Gem diamonds are graded according to weight, color, purity, and cut. The weight of the diamond is measured in carats. One carat weight is 200 mg [0.007 oz]. The color of most diamonds in jewelry has a faint tint of yellow. Very few diamonds are colorless. A few contain a slight blue tint. Diamonds can be a number of other colors, but such diamonds are usually not as valuable. The value of a diamond can be lessened by many kinds of flaws. These flaws include the presence of foreign material (which may affect the color), small bubbles, and small cracks. The cracks are called fissures, or sometimes feathers. The cut of a diamond affects its value. Diamonds that are not properly cut do not have as much brilliance as the ones that are.

Famous diamonds   There are hundreds of famous diamonds, each with an interesting history. Many diamonds are the property of royalty or governments. The largest cut diamond in existence was once part of the Cullinan, a stone that weighed 3,106 carats, or about 0.6 kg [1.3 lbs]. The Cullinan was purchased by the Transvaal Government of South Africa and presented to King Edward VII of Britain. Cutters in Amsterdam later trimmed the Cullinan into nine large stones and 96 smaller stones. The largest of these is the largest cut diamond in the world.

Diamonds used in industry   Industrial diamonds include stones that are not of gem quality. Such diamonds are used to cut, grind, and bore very hard materials. Sometimes whole rough diamonds are set into tools. Other times the diamonds are crushed, mixed with a binder, and baked on to a tool surface. A diamond-tipped needle is used in some record players.

Artificial diamonds   There is not a large enough supply of natural diamonds to meet the needs of industry. For this reason, industry depends on artificial diamonds. The first artificial diamonds were made in 1955 by scientists at the General Electric Research Laboratory. Tiny diamonds, no larger than a grain of sand, were made by subjecting carbon to extremely high pressure and temperatures. Today, several companies manufacture industrial diamonds. In 1970, the General Electric Company produced the first artificial diamonds of gem quality and size. Artificial

diamonds are not sold as jewelry. They cost too much to produce—much more than natural diamonds themselves.

Imitation diamonds   Imitation diamonds, made from several substances under various trade names, are made into gem stones that resemble genuine diamonds. Imitation diamonds do not have the hardness of real diamonds, and soon show scratches and other signs of wear.   J.J.A./R.H.

DIAPHRAGM (dī′ ə fram′) The diaphragm is a sheet of muscle located in the chest cavity. It is important in the process of breathing.

The diaphragm separates the chest from the abdomen. When relaxed, it curves up like a dome at the center, allowing the lungs to exhale. When it contracts, it flattens and increases the volume of the chest. During contraction, it causes air to be drawn into the lungs. This action of moving air in and out of the lungs by contraction and relaxation of the diaphragm is called breathing. *See also* RESPIRATION.   P.G.C./J.J.F.

DIATOM (dī′ ə täm′) The diatoms are a class of more than 5,000 species of golden brown algae. They may live in salt or fresh water. They may live in groups or chains, or live alone. These one-celled organisms are considered plants because they have cell walls and are able to produce their own food. (*See* CELL; PHOTOSYNTHESIS.) Diatoms, however, are able to move from one place to another by a series of jerky or creeping motions. Their cell walls contain large amounts of silica, forming a shell-like protective coat.

Diatoms are an important part of plankton which serves as a major food source for many sea animals. The shells of diatoms collect at the bottoms of lakes, oceans, and ponds. This diatomaceous earth, or diatomite, is used as insulation, as a filtering agent for swimming pools, as an abrasive, and as part of some explosives.   A.J.C./M.H.S.

DICOTYLEDON (dī′ kät′ əl ēd′ ən) Dicotyledons are one of two major classes of flowering plants. (*See* MONOCOTYLEDON.) The more than 250,000 species are characterized by seeds which have two cotyledons storing food for the embryo. Most dicotyledons are woody plants with separate bundles of xylem and phloem. Xylem, carrying water and dissolved minerals from the roots to the leaves, is separated from the phloem, carrying food from the leaves to the roots, by a layer of cambium. The cambium produces both the xylem and the phloem. The yearly production of xylem causes an increase in the thickness of the trunk and branches. (*See* ANNUAL RING.)

Branching is more common in dicotyledons than in monocotyledons. The leaves are usually broad with a network of veins. Flower parts (petals, sepals, stamens, and pistils) are usually in multiples of four of five. *See also* ANGIOSPERM. A.J.C./M.H.S.

This semiautomated machine manufactures punches that are used to make holes in a variety of materials.

DIE (dī) A die is a kind of tool used in shaping, cutting, trimming, and casting various materials. Many manufactured products require the use of dies.

Many types of dies are used in the manufacture of automobiles. The body parts of cars are formed in dies. These dies are built so that the top and bottom parts are of the same shape. There is only enough space between the top and bottom sections of the die to allow for a sheet of metal. When the metal is placed in the die, pressure is applied. The sheet takes the form of the die.

After the part is formed, it is removed and trimmed in a blanking die. A blanking die is like a pair of scissors. One blade passes another so that it cuts the metal instead of shaping it.

In making automobile trim, an extrusion die is used. The metal is forced through a hole in the die. The strip of metal that is pulled through is the shape of the opening in the die. Other trim parts are made of die castings. These dies are made in a different way. (*See* CASTING.)

Automobile making is only one example of the many uses of dies. A cookie cutter is a simple type of die. The pictures impressed on coins are formed with dies. Buttons, plastic toys, doorknobs, and certain jars are a few of the products used every day that are shaped with dies. J.J.A./R.W.L.

DIESEL (dē′ zəl) A diesel engine is a type of internal combustion engine that is used for heavy-duty work. It uses low-cost oil for fuel, and usually has a long life. Railroad locomotives, trailer trucks, buses, tractors, and road building equipment are powered by diesel engines. Ships and electric power generating stations also use diesel engines. Small models are used to power some automobiles. The diesel engine was developed in 1897 by

Rudolf Diesel was a German engineer.

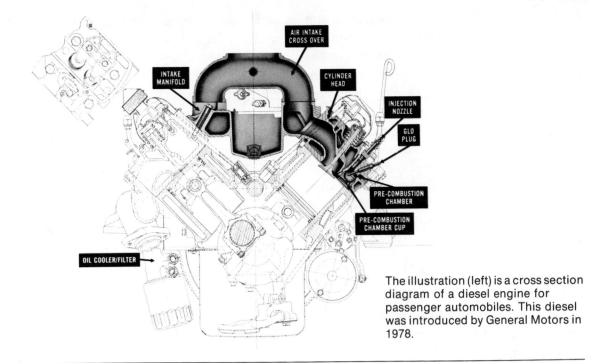

The illustration (left) is a cross section diagram of a diesel engine for passenger automobiles. This diesel was introduced by General Motors in 1978.

Rudolf Diesel, a German engineer.

The diesel engine differs from the gasoline engine in two main ways. The diesel is a compression-ignition engine, whereas the gasoline engine is a spark-ignition engine. In a diesel engine, air is compressed in each cylinder, causing its temperatures to rise. Fuel is then injected into the cylinders. The heat of the air causes the mixture to ignite and to explode. Gasoline engines use electric sparks to ignite the fuel and air mixtures in the cylinders. (*See* ENGINE.) Diesel engines use low-grade fuel oils that require less refining than gasoline and are less expensive.

Pressure of over 10,500 kilonewtons per square meter [1,500 lbs per square in] is built up in the cylinder of a diesel engine by compression and the subsequent explosion, or combustion. This pressure forces the piston downwards, which turns the crankshaft. Cylinder walls and most other parts of diesel engines are thicker and stronger than those parts in gasoline engines so they can stand the extra strains and stresses.

There are two main types of diesel engines, the four-stroke engine and the two-stroke engine. In the four-stroke model, which is the larger and more powerful of the two, each piston moves down, up, down, and up to complete a cycle. The first downstroke draws air into the cylinder. The first upstroke compresses the air. The second downstroke is the power stroke. The second upstroke exhausts the gases produced by combustion.

In a two-stroke diesel engine, the exhaust and intake of air occur through openings in the cylinder near the end of the power stroke. The one upstroke is the compression stroke. The downstroke is the power stroke. Two-stroke engines have twice as many power strokes per cycle as four-stroke engines. Two-stroke engines are used for applications that require high power in a small engine. *See also* ENGINE; LOCOMOTIVE.   W.R.P./J.T.

DIET

Diet (dī′ ət) is all the food and drink that a person normally consumes on a regular, daily basis. Food is needed to build and maintain body tissues, to provide a source of energy for all body functions, and to provide the chemicals necessary for regulating the processes of the body. A person's dietary needs vary according to age, weight, physical condition, body metabolism, amount of activity, and the climate. The energy content of food, as well as the amount of energy expended by the body, are measured in units called calories. If a person consumes more calories than he uses, he will gain weight. If he consumes fewer calories than he uses, he will lose weight. Since a balanced diet provides all the necessary nutrients in the proper amounts, a person following such a diet should neither gain nor lose weight. A balanced diet must include proteins, carbohydrates, fats, minerals, vitamins, and water.

Artificial protein may soon help solve world food problems. It is made from microorganisms.

Proteins are complex substances which are needed to build and repair tissues and to help in the production of hormones and enzymes. Proteins must be broken down into amino acids before they can be used by the body. (*See* DIGESTION.) The human body itself produces several amino acids, but the other, essential amino acids must be supplied by foods in the diet. Meat, fish, seafood, and eggs are good sources of most or all of the essential amino acids. Vegetables, cereals, and nuts provide many of the essential amino

acids, but must be varied and eaten in larger quantities if they alone are to meet the body's protein needs.

Carbohydrates are the main source of energy for the body. Although they supply fewer calories per unit weight than do fats, carbohydrates are broken down more easily. Carbohydrates become simple sugars through the process of digestion. Fruits, vegetables, cereals, bread, pastries, and macaroni products are major sources of carbohydrates.

Fats, or lipids, are used mostly for energy, but they do function in other ways in the body. Fats are broken down into fatty acids and glycerol. Since the body tends to use carbohydrates before it uses fats, fats are often stored for use at a later time. Fats may be in solid form as in butter, meats, and fish, or in liquid form as in oils.

Minerals are important in the diet as they help regulate the body and are elements in many vital chemical compounds used by the body. Some of the most important minerals are calcium, phosphorous, iron, sodium, potassium, chlorine, and iodine. Calcium and phosphorous are used in bones and teeth, and in regulating body processes. Milk products and leafy green vegetables are good sources of these minerals. Iron is needed for hemoglobin in the blood. Sources of iron include lean meats, eggs, beans, and leafy green vegetables. Sodium, potassium, and chlorine all function in the regulation of cellular activity. Most foods, and regular table salt, supply these minerals. (*See* SODIUM CHLORIDE.) Iodine is needed for the proper functioning of the thyroid gland. Iodine is often added to table salt.

Vitamins have many important regulatory functions in the body. Vitamins are found in most foods, though only a carefully balanced diet can supply the necessary vitamins in the proper amounts. Many people add organic or synthetic vitamins to their diets.

Water makes up most of the human body. All body processes and functions require

DIET TABLES

The three main components of foods are proteins, carbohydrates and fats. Protein is the most vital part of our diet because it builds up the body tissues. Fats and carbohydrates both provide energy and heat. Carbohydrate-rich foods contain a lot of starch and sugar which are of little value to our bodies.

The energy value of food is measured in units of heat called Calories. People who do energetic jobs use up several thousand Calories each day, but those who only sit at desks use up very few. Table 1 shows the number of Calories in average helpings of various foods and drinks. It also shows whether the food is mainly protein, fat or carbohydrate.

In addition to protein and fat, the body needs various vitamins and minerals. A person who lacks certain of these may develop a deficiency disease. Table 2 shows what types of foods contain the four most important vitamins.

It is important not to allow yourself to become too heavy. Some people have larger frames than others and naturally weigh more. But there are certain weight limits which you exceed only at risk to your health. Table 3 shows the average weights of men and women wearing light clothing.

The fewer Calories you take in your food, the less likely you are to gain weight. If you wish to lose weight it is essential to check carefully the Calorie content of your meals. You should set a target for each day. Some people can slim more rapidly than others. But in any case you should not take fewer than 1,000 Calories a day.

Table 1

Food	Protein	Fat	Carbohydrate	Calories (average helping)
APPLE			√	30
BACON	√	√		350
BEEF STEAK	√	√		320
BEER (0.2 liters)			√	90
BISCUITS			√	120
BREAD (slice)			√	80
BUTTER		√	√	100
CHEESE	√	√		120
CHOCOLATE		√	√	250
COD	√			110
COFFEE, WHITE			√	100
EGG, BOILED	√	√		80
ICE CREAM		√	√	100
LAMB, ROAST	√	√		250
MILK (0.5 liters)	√	√		380
ORANGE			√	40
PEAS	√		√	60
POTATOES			√	100
RICE			√	130
SHELLFISH	√			70
ALCOHOL		—none—		70
SUGAR			√	110
TEA			√	70

Table 2

Name	Good Sources
Vitamin A	Fish liver oil, liver, eggs, milk, vegetables
Vitamin B	Yeast, liver, milk, eggs, meat, green vegetables
Vitamin C	Fresh fruit and vegetables
Vitamin D	Fish liver oil, eggs, milk, sunlight on skin

Table 3

MEN Height m	(ft in)	Weight kg	(lb)	WOMEN Height m	(ft in)	Weight kg	(lb)
1.51	(5 0)	57.3	(126)	1.41	(4 8)	50.9	(112)
1.54	(5 1)	58.2	(128)	1.44	(4 9)	51.9	(114)
1.57	(5 2)	59.1	(130)	1.47	(4 10)	52.7	(116)
1.59	(5 3)	60.6	(133)	1.49	(4 11)	53.6	(118)
1.62	(5 4)	61.9	(136)	1.51	(5 0)	54.5	(120)
1.64	(5 5)	63.8	(140)	1.54	(5 1)	55.5	(122)
1.67	(5 6)	65.6	(144)	1.57	(5 2)	56.5	(124)
1.69	(5 7)	67.2	(148)	1.59	(5 3)	57.6	(127)
1.72	(5 8)	69.0	(152)	1.62	(5 4)	59.5	(131)
1.74	(5 9)	71.0	(156)	1.64	(5 5)	61.0	(134)
1.77	(5 10)	73.2	(161)	1.67	(5 6)	62.6	(138)
1.79	(5 11)	75.6	(166)	1.69	(5 7)	64.5	(142)
1.82	(6 0)	78.4	(172)	1.72	(5 8)	66.4	(146)
1.84	(6 1)	81.0	(178)	1.74	(5 9)	68.1	(150)
1.87	(6 2)	83.8	(184)	1.77	(5 10)	70.0	(154)
1.89	(6 3)	86.4	(190)	1.79	(5 11)	71.4	(157)
1.92	(6 4)	89.0	(196)	1.82	(6 0)	73.1	(161)

Table 4

Four Major Food Groups

Milk Group: milk, butter, cheese, ice cream, eggs
Meat Group: meat, fish, seafood
Vegetable-Fruit Group: vegetables, fruits, nuts
Bread-Cereal Group: bread, cereals, pastries, desserts

water. Water is found in all foods except those that are specially dehydrated.

The four groups of food Food is usually divided into four groups. The milk group includes dairy products such as eggs, cheese, milk, butter, and ice cream. The meat group includes meat, fish, and seafood. The vegetable-fruit group includes vegetables, fruits, and nuts. This group also supplies the major portion of roughage, or indigestible fibrous parts of the food which give bulk to material moving through the alimentary canal. The bread-cereal group includes breads, cereals and grain products, pastries, and desserts. A balanced diet usually contains foods from each of these groups. It is possible, however, to have a balanced diet even though one of these groups may be eliminated. For example, vegetarians who eat planned meals are able to consume all the necessary nutrients without having to consume meat.

Special diets Although people's food needs are generally similar, certain people need special diets. These diets should be planned and supervised by a doctor or a dietician, a person who studies diets and dietary needs.

Children and teenagers need more calories than adults need. They use more calories because they are growing, and, in general, are more active than adults. Expectant and nursing mothers, elderly people, and people with certain illnesses all have special dietary requirements. A person with diabetes mellitus, for example, must regulate his sugar intake. People with heart, circulatory, or kidney problems are usually put on a low-salt diet. People who are allergic to or are unable to digest certain foods must eliminate these foods from their diets. (*See* ALLERGY.)

A person who is underweight can gain weight by increasing his calorie intake, usually by eating more carbohydrates. An overweight person must limit his calorie intake to lose weight. In recent years, there have been hundreds of "fad" or "miracle" weight-loss diets. In spite of all claims, the only way a diet can be effective is if it involves decreasing calorie intake and/or increasing calorie use (through more exercise). Fewer than 5% of the people who lose weight by following a "fad" weight-loss diet are able to keep the weight off for at least a year.

People in many countries suffer from diseases caused by a deficiency of one or more of the vital nutrients in the diet. Diets in developing countries are often deficient in protein. Some countries have had deficiencies of one or more minerals, which has resulted in many birth defects and other diseases. The diets of some people in the United States, particularly those of many teenagers, are deficient in certain nutrients. The ready availability of "junk food" which is high in calories but low in nutritional value, is thought to be a major reason for this problem.

Dietetics is the study of diets and dietary needs. As the dietary needs of the growing world population become better defined, scientists and dieticians are seeking new ways of meeting these needs. They are exploring potential new food sources, as well as trying to increase the productivity of current food sources. A.J.C./J.J.F.

DIFFERENTIAL (dif′ ə ren′ chəl) The differential is a system of gears that is mounted between the drive wheels of a vehicle. The gears make it possible for one drive wheel to turn faster than the other wheel when the vehicle goes around a corner. The differential gears are located inside a metal housing. They are turned by the drive shaft from the engine. Axles, or shafts, connected to the gears, extend out from each side of the housing to the wheels.

When the vehicle moves straight ahead, the differential gears divide the driving force equally between the two drive wheels. This keeps each wheel turning at the same speed.

However, when the car turns a corner, the gears permit the outside wheel, which has farther to travel, to turn faster than the inside wheel. Also, when a car gets stuck in snow or mud, the differential gears allow one wheel to spin while the other does not move.

The differential principle was developed in the early 1900s by Charles S. Mott and H. H. Timken, two American inventors.

Racing cars do not have differential gears because they cause a loss of power in the turns. Racing cars skid in the turns because both drive wheels turn at the same speed. *See also* AUTOMOBILE; GEAR.   W.R.P./J.T.

DIFFERENTIATION, CELLULAR

Cellular differentiation (dif′ ə ren′ chē ā′ shən) is a process that occurs in all multicellular plants and animals. In this process one cell develops into many distinct types of cells in the growing embryo. A fertilized egg cell (zygote) or a spore develops into an adult by dividing many times in a process called mitosis. As the number of cells increases, the cells begin to develop into distinct types of cells with specific functions. The controlling process of differentiation which determines whether a certain cell becomes a muscle cell or a nerve cell, for example, is not understood.

It is known that heredity accounts for an organism's producing other organisms similar to itself. For example, a cat will always give birth to another cat, not to a dog or a rabbit. Heredity is ultimately controlled by DNA. Each cell of an organism has exactly the same kind of DNA molecule with exactly the same genetic code as every other cell. For some reason, the DNA directs certain cells to develop in certain ways. Since the DNA in every cell of that organism is exactly the same, however, it is difficult to understand why cells are different from one another. This mystery is especially interesting when one considers that of the billions and billions of cells in the human body, there are thousands of different types performing thousands of

different functions, yet they all have the same DNA code. *See also* CHROMOSOME; CLONE; GENE; GENETICS; GROWTH.   A.J.C./E.R.L.

DIFFRACTION

(dif rak′ shən) Diffraction is the spreading out of waves as they pass by the edge of an obstacle, which is anything that stands in the way of the waves. Diffraction is also the spreading out of waves as they pass through an opening.

Diffraction happens as water waves spread out in all directions after passing through a narrow channel. Diffraction also explains why sound can be heard around a corner, even though there is no straight path from the source of the sound to the ear.

Diffraction of light differs from that of sound. Diffraction of light is most evident when the obstacle is about the same size as the wavelength diffracted. The sound waves we hear have wavelengths of about a meter [a yard]. These waves are diffracted by ordinary objects. Visible light waves, however, have wavelengths of less than .0007 mm [.000028 in]. Light waves therefore can be diffracted only by very small objects.

When light passes the edge of an obstacle, and then falls onto a screen, a sharp edged shadow does not appear. A bending in the light appears to take place at the edge of the obstacle. This spreads light into what otherwise would be a dark shadow. This is, however, a very small effect, and is difficult to observe.

The occurrence of diffraction has been used as a test to see whether or not certain things are waves. For example, diffraction of x-rays by crystals convinced scientists that x-rays are waves. (*See* X-RAY DIFFRACTION.)

A diffraction grating is a small glass plate with lines ruled on it at very small, equal intervals. Light can pass only between the lines, and the openings between the lines are about as wide as a wavelength of light. If a beam of white light strikes the grating, a pattern of light of the various spectrum colors appears on a screen behind the grating. The colors appear because white light is made up of different colors. These colors have different wavelengths, and the longer wavelengths are diffracted at greater angles. Scientists can identify a substance by the pattern of colors that the substance produces when light passes through a diffraction grating or a prism. *See also* INTERFERENCE; SPECTROSCOPE; WAVES.

J.J.A./S.S.B.

DIFFUSION (dif yü′ zhən) When a small amount of sugar is placed in a glass of water, it dissolves and spreads through the water so that every part tastes equally sweet. This process of substances mingling with each other is called diffusion.

When the sugar starts to dissolve, the water close to it soon stops taking it into solution. It is saturated. However, the sugar molecules are moving about in all directions, being jostled by each other and by the water molecules. Some sugar molecules move away from the sugar into fresh water, and are replaced by more molecules from the sugar. Soon all the sugar has dissolved. But as long as any parts of the water are richer in dissolved sugar than other parts, more sugar molecules move out of these parts than are moving in. In the end, the sugar molecules are spread evenly throughout the substance.

The molecules in gases, such as air, are farther apart than the molecules in liquids and solids, and they have higher speeds. Therefore, diffusion occurs more rapidly in gases than liquids. If a bottle of perfume is opened in a room, the odor is soon spread throughout the room. The same thing is true of the smell of many flowers. These odors come from gases whose molecules have mixed with the molecules of the other gases in the air.

In plants, diffusion takes place when sap passes through cell walls. (*See* OSMOSIS.) When light shines on a rough surface, the rays are diffused, or reflected in many directions. Diffused light is good light to read under. It does not give off much glare.

Diffusion must not be confused with other forces making particles move. Electrons and ions are electrically charged and usually move toward opposite charges. The air around the earth does not vary much in composition, except where gases are being released into it. This is due partly to diffusion and partly to winds. In a similar way, oceans are kept fairly uniform in composition by diffusion and by currents.

Thermal diffusion is a special process whereby heavy atoms or molecules in a gas move toward colder regions. This process is used to separate isotopes in the nuclear power industry.

J.J.A./A.D.

DIGESTION (dī jes′ chən) All animals must eat food in order to live. The food is used as fuel in the cells to produce energy. Food cannot be used as fuel when it sits on a dinner plate. It must be eaten and converted to the proper form. This conversion, which takes place inside the body, is called digestion. In single-celled animals, digestion takes place in small cavities called vacuoles. Members of the phylum Cnidaria bring food in and take waste out of the same opening. Advanced animals, such as humans, have a complex digestion system. Food enters through the mouth and wastes leave through the anus. Digestion occurs between these two places. (*See* ALIMENTARY CANAL.)

Digestion in humans Digestion begins in the mouth. Chewing makes food soft and breaks it into small pieces. The saliva in the mouth helps break down some carbohydrates into sugars. Saliva also makes the food slippery so that it can slide down the throat—or esophagus—easily. A wavelike muscle contraction called peristalsis pushes the food down to the stomach. Churning of the stomach changes the food into a semi-liquid mass called chyme. At this time, gastric juices, produced by the stomach wall, start

DIGESTIVE JUICES IN MAN

NAME	ACTION
Saliva	
Ptyalin	Digests starch to maltose
Gastric juice	
*Hydrochloric acid	Converts pepsinogen to pepsin
Pepsin (formed from pepsinogen)	Digests proteins to peptides
Rennin	Coagulates casein (milk protein)
Bile	
*Bile salts	Emulsify fats
Intestinal juice	
Amylase	Digests starch to maltose
Enterokinase	Converts trypsinogen to trypsin
Exopeptidases	Digests peptides to amino acids
Lactase	Digests lactose to glucose and fructose
Lipase	Digests emulsified fats to fatty acids and glycerol
Maltase	Digests maltose to glucose and fructose
Sucrase (invertase)	Digests sucrose to glucose and fructose
Pancreatic juice	
*Alkali	Neutralizes stomach acids
Amylase	Digests starch to maltose
Chymotrypsin	Digests proteins to peptides
Exopeptidases	Digests peptides to amino acids
Lipase	Digests emulsified fats to fatty acids and glycerol
Trypsin	Digests proteins to peptides and converts chymotrypsinogen to chymotrypsin

*All the substances listed above are enzymes except those marked with an asterisk.

digesting, or breaking down the food into usable forms. Gastric juice contains hydrochloric acid. Liquid food passes out of the stomach and into the small intestine. (*See* INTESTINE.) Enzymes are added there. Most of the food is broken down in the small intestine into its simplest forms: sugar, amino acids, and fats. These nutrients are absorbed by little fingerlike projections called microvilli. From there the nutrients enter the blood and are transported throughout the body to every cell. (*See* CIRCULATORY SYSTEM.)

Not all of the material that is eaten is absorbed by the body as nutrients. Some of it is unusable to the body. As it passes into the large intestine, water is removed and saved by the body. The rest of the waste product is passed out of the body as feces through the anus.

After the food is eaten, several hours pass before its nutrients are in the cells providing energy. The body provides enough food to each cell to meet its present need. If there is more food than is necessary, it is stored as fat. If a person always eats more than his body needs, his body will store a lot of fat. The person will be overweight. When a person does not eat enough food, his body will use up stored fat. If a person always eats less food than his body needs, he will be underweight.

S.R.G./J.J.F.

DIGITAL COMPUTER *See* COMPUTER.

The band of dark rock in the center of the photograph is a dike of igneous rock. In a molten state, it was forced up through the rock layers.

DIKE (dīk) The word dike has several meanings. In the Netherlands, dikes are dams that hold back the sea. They allow land to be used that would otherwise be covered by water.

In geology, dikes are bands of igneous rocks. They are usually at a steep angle to the preexisting rock surrounding it. Dikes have a wide range of size. When there is a large number of dikes in an area, they are called a dike swarm. *See also* SILL.   J.M.C./W.R.S.

DINGO (ding′ gō) The dingo (*Canis dingo*) is a wild dog found only in Australia. It was probably introduced to the continent about 10,000 years ago by aborigines from New Guinea and Asia. It is thought that dingoes were once tame dogs that escaped and reverted to their wild state. Dingo puppies, however, can be trained and make good pets.

Like all dogs, the dingo is a carnivorous mammal. (*See* CARNIVORE.) The dingo stands about 50 cm [20 in] tall at the shoulder, and has an alert face, erect ears, and a bushy tail. Its fur is usually yellowish brown, but may vary from light yellow to black.

Dingoes usually howl instead of bark. They hunt alone or in small family groups. They prey on small marsupials, such as the wallaby, as well as on livestock. Because dingoes frequently attack sheep, the Australian government considers them pests and has tried to eliminate completely the dingo population.   A.J.C./J.J.M.

DINOSAUR

Dinosaur (dī′ nə sȯr′) is the common name for two types of giant reptiles that lived millions of years ago. The word dinosaur comes from the Greek words meaning "terrible lizard."

Brontosaurus (below) was a huge, plant-eating dinosaur. Until recently, scientists thought that it lived mainly in water to support its weight. Evidence now suggests that it was a land animal.

Dinosaurs lived during the Mesozoic era, which started about 225 million years ago, and lasted about 160 million years. The Mesozoic era is divided into three periods: the Triassic, the Jurassic, and the Cretaceous. Dinosaurs were common by the end of the Triassic period. They dominated the earth during the Jurassic period and most of the Cretaceous period. They died out during the last part of the Cretaceous period.

Dinosaurs probably evolved from the thecodonts. These were reptiles about 1 meter [3.3 ft] long which appeared early in the Triassic period. They were the first reptiles to walk on their hind legs. At the end of the Triassic period, dinosaurs were common, and their fossils have been found in many parts of the world.

Dinosaurs varied greatly in size. Some were the size of chickens, while others weighed more than 45 metric tons [50 tons]. Some dinosaurs continued to walk on their hind legs, while others walked on all four legs. Many dinosaurs had smooth skin, but some had scaly skin, and still others were armored with large bony plates. Some

Skeletons of a dinosaur called Iguanodon are in many museums. It was so named because of its lizard, or iguanalike, hip bone.

dinosaurs ate meat and others ate plants. One feature, however, that all dinosaurs had in common was a tiny brain.

Classification of dinosaurs The word dinosaur is not used by scientists anymore because it refers to two very different orders, or groups, of reptiles. Both groups belong to a major group called Archosauria, which means ''ruling reptiles.'' The reptiles of Archosauria are divided into two orders by the structure of their pelvis or hipbone. The two orders are Saurischia, or lizard-hipped, and Ornithischia, or bird-hipped.

The saurischians The lizard-hipped saurischians are divided into two groups: the sauropods, or plant-eaters, and the theropods, or meat-eaters.

The sauropods were the largest dinosaurs. They include the massive Brontosaurus. This huge creature grew to lengths of 24 m [80 ft] and weighed about 32 metric tons [35 tons]. The Brontosaurus probably spent much of its time eating in the huge swamps that existed then. All of the sauropods had long necks and tails and walked on all four legs. Even larger than the Brontosaurus was the Brachiosaurus, largest of all the dinosaurs. The Brachiosaurus weighed 77 metric tons [85 tons] and was 21 m [70 ft] long.

The meat-eating theropods walked on their hind legs. They used their very short front legs for grabbing and tearing food. The tall and terrible theropods hunted the plant-eating sauropods. The Tyrannosaurus was the largest meat-eating animal ever to live on the earth. It was 6 m [20 ft] tall and had teeth that were 15 cm [6 in] long. Its head was larger than that of most dinosaurs, and its front legs were too small to be of any use.

The ornithischians The bird-hipped ornithischians included both the armor-plated dinosaurs and the duck-billed dinosaurs.

The Stegosaurus was an ornithischian that

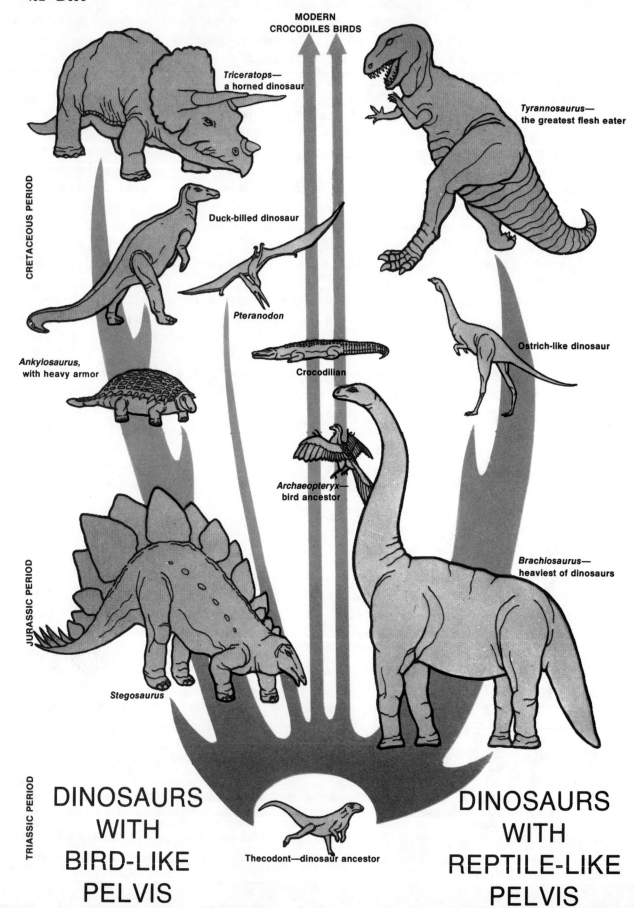

MODERN
CROCODILES BIRDS

Triceratops—
a horned dinosaur

Tyrannosaurus—
the greatest flesh eater

CRETACEOUS PERIOD

Duck-billed dinosaur

Pteranodon

Ankylosaurus,
with heavy armor

Crocodilian

Ostrich-like dinosaur

Archaeopteryx—
bird ancestor

JURASSIC PERIOD

Brachiosaurus—
heaviest of dinosaurs

Stegosaurus

TRIASSIC PERIOD

DINOSAURS WITH BIRD-LIKE PELVIS

Thecodont—dinosaur ancestor

DINOSAURS WITH REPTILE-LIKE PELVIS

An illustration (facing left) of the family tree of dinosaurs divides their evolution into the Triassic period, the Jurassic period, and Cretaceous period.

had bony plates of armor protecting its neck, back, and tail. These plates were used as defense against the meat-eating dinosaurs. The Stegosaurus is sometimes said to have had two brains: one tiny brain in its head and another much larger nerve center that controlled its tail and hind legs.

The only ornithischians to walk on two legs were the Ornithopods. They had webbed feet and could swim, and many had duck-billed mouths.

Another ornithischian was the Triceratops. This dinosaur resembled the rhinoceros because of its large horns.

Dinosaur extinction   The disappearance of dinosaurs 65 million years ago is an unsolved mystery. Some scientists had thought that the breakup of the continents was responsible. (*See* CONTINENTAL DRIFT.) A reduction in dry-land habitat, along with a worldwide rise in sea level, might have caused environmental changes the dinosaurs could not adapt to. But geologists have recently begun finding evidence of a catastrophic impact from outer space, leading them to a new theory of extinction. They think that there was a meteor impact so powerful that enough debris was thrown into the atmosphere to blot out the sun for many months. Without sunlight, many photosynthesizing organisms, and the animals directly dependent on them, would have died out. In this way, dinosaurs, at the top of the food chain, would have been forced to compete for a much reduced food supply and would have lost to smaller animals which need less food to survive.   J.M.C./R.J.B.

DIOECIOUS (dī ē′ shəs) Dioecious refers to a condition of higher plants in which a plant has either male flowers or female flowers, but not both. Male flowers are staminate, having stamens but no pistils. Female flowers are pistillate, having pistils but no stamens. A dioecious plant is either male or female, and it is unable to pollinate itself. (*See* POLLINATION.) *See also* ANGIOSPERM; MONOECIOUS.
A.J.C./M.H.S.

DIOPTER (dī äp′ tər) A diopter is a unit representing the power of magnification of a lens. It is found by dividing the focal length (f) of the lens, in meters, into 1 meter. For example, if the focal length of a certain lens is equal to 20 cm, or 0.2 meters, the power of the lens is equal to 1/0.2 diopters, or 5 diopters. *See also* CAMERA; LENS.   J.M.C./S.S.B.

DIRECT CURRENT (də rekt′ kər′ ənt) Direct current is electric current that always flows in one direction. It is produced by batteries and direct current (DC) generators. Direct current operates automobile electric systems, locomotives, and some types of motors used in industry. Radios, television sets and other electronic devices use alternating current as their primary source of power. (See ALTERNATING CURRENT.) However, they also need some direct current to operate internal circuits. Devices called rectifiers change alternating current into direct current for these circuits. *See also* CURRENT, ELECTRIC; RECTIFIER.   W.R.P./A.I.

DIRIGIBLE (dir′ ə jə bəl) A dirigible is a rigid, lighter-than-air aircraft shaped like a cigar. Dirigibles were built and flown by people in many countries during the early 1900s. Dirigibles had their own motive power in the form of gasoline engine-driven propellers, and they could be steered in any direction by their crews by means of control surfaces. They also carried passengers and freight. Some dirigibles, particularly those built in Germany, were 240 m [800 ft] long and 30 m [100 ft] in diameter. The body of a dirigible consisted of a framework of aluminum girders covered by linen cloth. Large bags containing hydrogen, a lighter-than-air and highly flammable gas, were located inside the framework. The hydrogen provided the lift for the dirigible. The crew and passengers rode in compartments in a gondola attached to the bottom of the airship's body.

Count Ferdinand von Zeppelin, a retired German army officer, designed and built over 25 dirigibles. Many people called dirigibles zeppelins because of the Count's involvement. He built his first dirigible in 1900. It was called the LZ–1. It was nearly 128 m [420 ft] long, and it contained 9,910 cu m [350,000 cu ft] of hydrogen. The LZ–1 was propelled by two engines that drove four-bladed propellers. Von Zeppelin established an airline in 1910 and used his dirigibles to carry more than 35,000 passengers between German cities from 1910 to 1914—the beginning of World War I. During WWI, Germany made use of von Zeppelin's dirigibles to drop bombs on English cities.

In 1929, the Germans built the *Graf Zeppelin,* a giant dirigible that was 240 m [800 ft] long and 30 m [100 ft] in diameter. It carried 50 passengers and could fly at 110 kph [70 mph]. The *Graf Zeppelin* flew around the world in 21 days and made regular flights from Germany to South America from 1933 to 1937.

The success of the *Graf Zeppelin* led to the building of the *Hindenburg* in 1936. It was the largest dirigible ever built, 247 m [812 ft] long. The *Hindenburg* made 36 flights across the Atlantic Ocean from Germany to the United States. During a routine landing at Lakehurst, New Jersey, on May 6, 1937, it burst into flames and was destroyed. Over 30 people were killed in the disaster.

The tragedy ended the era of the dirigible. The U.S., England, Soviet Union, and Italy had all previously built and flown dirigibles, most of which were abandoned after the *Hindenburg* fire. Aviation experts talked about building dirigibles again in the 1970s because of the availability of helium, a lighter-than-air gas that does not burn. However, none were built. *See also* AVIATION, HISTORY OF.   W.R.P./J.V.P.

DISEASE

A disease (diz ēz′) is a condition of a living thing that prevents it from functioning in a normal way. When your body does not seem to be working normally and you feel sick, you may have a disease.

When you see a doctor about feeling sick, he or she looks for signs that show what kind of disease you might have. The doctor is doing a kind of detective work for which he or she has been specially trained. When the doctor finds out what is wrong with you, your disease has been diagnosed.

We can put different diseases together into groups according to what causes them. There are infections caused by "germs." These are living organisms growing inside your body. There are several kinds of germs, including bacteria, viruses, and fungi.

Bacteria cause diseases like sore throat, whooping cough, and scarlet fever. They are easy to treat with antibiotics and can be prevented by vaccines.

Viruses cause many diseases, including measles, mumps, certain types of influenza (flu), acquired immune deficiency syndrome (AIDS), and poliomyelitis (polio). Some virus diseases can be prevented by vaccines. But antibiotics will not cure most virus-type diseases.

Several diseases, like athlete's foot and ringworm, are caused by fungi. These are skin diseases and are difficult to treat.

Many of these diseases are contagious and can spread from one person to another through the air. Measles is very contagious and can spread among people rapidly.

Some infections are not contagious, but must be carried from person to person by

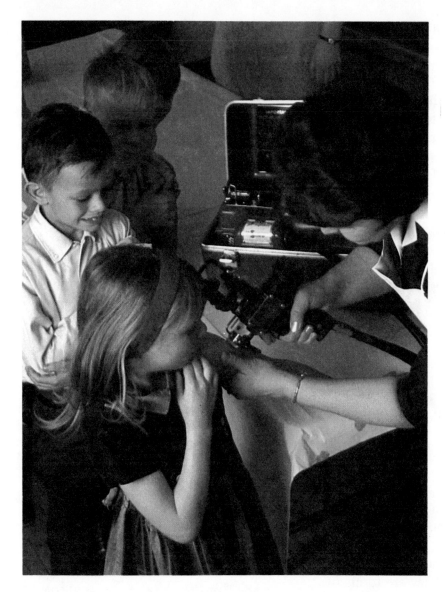

Smallpox is a dangerous virus disease which was once worldwide. It is very contagious. An international immunization program spearheaded by the United Nations has eradicated the disease. The photograph (left) shows children being immunized with a vaccination gun.

A mosquito sucks blood from a human finger. In this way, the anopheles mosquito spreads malaria by infecting blood with the parasite plasmodium.

animals or insects. Typhus and bubonic plague are spread by certain lice and fleas. Malaria can be carried only by certain mosquitoes. Other types of infections can be carried by larger organisms, like worms. These organisms are called parasites. One type that attacks people is the tapeworm. It grows in the intestines and can reach 4.6 m [15 ft] in length. The tapeworm eats the person's food, causing weakness in the person.

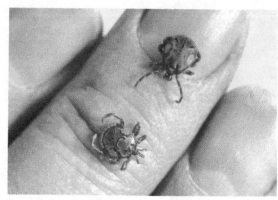

Ticks are bloodsucking arachnids which feed both on humans and domestic animals. They cause irritation and may transmit diseases, especially to cattle.

Many diseases result from the failure of organs in the body, like the heart, lungs, or kidneys, to work properly.

Diseases can also be due to neoplasms, called tumors or cancers. They are forms of growth of body tissue that are not normal. Cancers can be malignant and extremely serious. They can kill other tissues and spread throughout the body to various organs. A cancer can kill the person, unless it is diagnosed early and treated successfully. When a cancer does not spread, it is called benign.

If dust makes you sneeze, or some kind of food makes you itch, you may have an allergy. An allergy is a reaction to a substance you may touch or eat. Many people are allergic to bee stings, but can be treated with the proper drugs.

Certain diseases are inherited by the child from its parents. In many cases, doctors are not certain just what part heredity plays in disease. P.G.C./J.J.F.

DISINFECTANT (dis′ ən fek′ tənt) A disinfectant is a chemical that kills germs on nonliving objects. Disinfectants are used in hospitals to sterilize instruments and in operating rooms used for surgery. (*See* STERILIZATION.) They are also used in homes, particularly in kitchens and bathrooms. Household disinfectants are often mixed with detergents to help them clean while killing germs. Some countries add disinfectants to sewage systems and water supplies to help prevent epidemics.

Some common disinfectants are alcohol, ammonia, chlorine bleach, hexachlorophene, and iodine. Iodine and other substances used to kill germs on living organisms are called antiseptics. A.J.C./J.J.F.

DISPERSION OF LIGHT (dis pər′ zhən uv līt) When a beam of white light passes through a prism, the different wavelengths of light disperse, or spread apart, into a band of colors called the spectrum. This dispersion of light occurs because white light is actually made up of lights of various colors, each of which has a different wavelength. The different wavelengths of light travel at different speeds when they enter materials such as glass or water. Because they travel at different speeds, the different wavelengths are all bent, or refracted, at different angles, causing them to disperse. (*See* REFRACTION OF LIGHT.) *See also* ABERRATION; COLOR; LENS.

A.J.C./S.S.B.

DISPERSION OF PLANTS (dis pər′ zhən uv plants) Plants (except some species of algae, bacteria, and fungi) are fixed in one place for most of their lives. These fixed plants have evolved special structures for spreading their spores or seeds. These spores and seeds have stored food supplies and protective coats, and can be carried away from the parent plant by various agents. These agents are the plants themselves (dehiscence), air, water, and animals.

In dehiscence, or dispersion by explosion, a seed-containing structure, such as a pod, bursts, shooting the seeds into the air. Depending on the weight of the seed and the force with which they are thrown, the seeds may land a few centimeters or many kilometers away from the parent plant. Violets, members of the pea family, mustard family, and balsam family, disperse their seeds in this manner.

In dispersion by air, the seeds are either very lightweight or have special structures to keep them afloat in the wind. Some grass seeds have been detected at heights of more than 1,000 m [3,300 ft]. Lightweight orchid seeds have been found great distances from the parent plant. (*See* ORCHID FAMILY.) Seeds of other plants, such as the dandelion and cattail, have puffy hairs that help them float through the air. The seeds of maple, ash, and box elder have structures like wings so the seeds act like small helicopters in the wind. Tumbleweeds are plants that grow in hot, dry areas. They break off from their roots easily and are rolled or ''tumbled'' across deserts and plains by the wind, releasing their seeds as they go.

For dispersion by water, the seeds must be waterproof and able to float. Mangroves and coconuts have floating seeds with tough coats. Shortly after a new island was formed in the Pacific Ocean by an underwater volcano, coconut plants were found growing in the sandy, volcanic soil.

For dispersion by animals, plants have evolved many structures. Some seeds have burrs or hooks which attach to clothing or fur. They can be carried great distances before falling off. (*See* COCKLE.) Some seeds, such as mistletoe, are enclosed in sticky berries. When a bird or animal eats these berries, the seed sticks to its feet, mouth, or body. Some seeds are enclosed in juicy, tasty fruits which are attractive to birds, animals, and human beings. These fruits (with the seeds) are eaten, but the seeds are not affected by the digestive system. (*See* DIGESTION.) The seeds are then passed out of the body in the feces. (*See* EXCRETION.) The seeds of many plants, such as grape, mulberry, pear, and others, are dispersed this way. Seeds of clover and cereal crops are often dispersed by grazing animals, such as cattle and sheep. Human beings often disperse seeds by discarding apple cores, peach pits, and other inedible seeds from juicy fruits. People frequently and unknowingly carry seeds great distances by airplane, automobile, or boat. The seeds may be hidden in clothing or baggage. *See also* ADAPTATION.

A.J.C./M.H.S.

Two plants which disperse their seeds by a splitting of the fruit are stocks (left) and violets (right). The spores and seeds of a plant can be carried away from the parent plant by various agents. These agents are the plants themselves (dehiscence), air, water, and animals.

DISSOCIATION (dis ō′ sē ā′ shən) Dissociation is the process of breaking down a compound into simpler molecules or ions. Under different conditions, these molecules or ions can usually recombine to form the original compound. In electrolytic dissociation, the addition of solvents (such as water) causes the molecules of the substance to break into charged particles called ions. Substances which dissociate into ions are called electrolytes. Electrolytes conduct electricity because these ions are able to move about freely. Dissociation helps explain this and other properties of electrolytes.

In thermal dissociation, heat energy is applied to a compound, causing it to break down into simpler molecules or atoms. For example, when ammonium chloride is heated, it breaks down into ammonia and hydrogen chloride. When this mixture is cooled, it forms ammonium chloride once again. In some cases, heat can be used to produce electrolytic dissociation. For example, when salts such as sodium chloride are melted, they conduct electricity. *See also* ELECTROLYSIS; SOLUTION AND SOLUBILITY.   A.J.C./A.D.

DISTILLATION (dis′ tə lā′ shən) Distillation is a process that separates a mixture into the liquids or solids of which it is made. It usually involves the change of a substance into a vapor, which is then condensed to its liquid form. (*See* CONDENSATION.) There are three main types of distillation: simple distillation, fractional distillation, and destructive distillation.

Simple distillation is used to obtain a pure solvent (a substance that dissolves another substance) from a solution. (*See* SOLUTION AND SOLUBILITY.) The solution is boiled, and the vapor that condenses consists of pure solvent. Distilled water is obtained in this way.

In fractional distillation, a mixture of liquids is separated in order to obtain each liquid separately. The liquid mixture is heated to the temperature at which one of the liquids boils. The resulting vapor is cooled until it condenses to give pure liquid. This process is repeated until all the liquids in the mixture have been separated. A water-alcohol mixture is subjected to fractional distillation when making distilled liquors, such as whiskey. Fractional distillation is an important procedure in the refinement of petroleum. (*See* PETROLEUM.)

In destructive distillation, solid substances are heated without air, and the resulting vapors are condensed. This method of distillation is used to make charcoal. A carbon-rich substance, like wood, is placed in an airtight oven. It is heated so that the hydrogen, nitrogen, and oxygen are removed. The black substance remaining at the end of the process is charcoal. In destructive distillation, unlike other kinds of distillation, chemical changes occur in the substance being heated. *See also* COKE.   J.M.C./J.M.

DISTRIBUTOR (dis trib′ yət ər) A distributor is a device that sends electricity to spark plugs in an internal combustion engine. The distributor is the ''brain'' of the ignition system of an engine. Spark plugs that ignite the fuel and air mixtures in individual cylinders need electrical charges in a certain sequence and at precise times. The distributor does this job.

The distributor is contained within a cylindrical housing. It is connected to each spark plug by individual wires which lead into the top of the housing. Inside the housing are a vertical drive shaft that is connected to the engine crankshaft, two breaker points, a rotor, and a capacitor.

Electricity for an internal combustion engine comes originally from the battery. However, most batteries supply electricity at 12 volts. This is not a high enough voltage to create the hot spark necessary to ignite the fuel and air mixture that is compressed in the cylinders. The distributor works with the coil to increase the voltage. The coil is a transformer located between the battery and the distributor. It is a cylindrical object that contains two coils of fine wire called the primary coil and the secondary coil. It increases the voltage of the electricity from the battery from 12 volts up to 15,000 to 20,000 volts. A cam (an uneven wheel) on the distributor drive shaft opens and closes the spring-loaded breaker points quickly. This interrupts the flow of low voltage current in the primary coil, which creates a surge of high voltage current in the secondary coil. The high voltage current returns to the distributor where it is sent to the spark plugs, one after another, by a rotating switch called the rotor. The rotor is mounted on the drive shaft.

The breaker points remain closed for less than five thousandths (5/1,000) of a second for each spark. The breaks in the primary circuit of the coil caused by the breaker points are timed to take place near the top of each piston's compression stroke. That is when the fuel and air mixture in the cylinder is compressed and ready for ignition. The high voltage charge sent to the spark plug by the distributor creates a hot spark when it jumps across the gap between the two electrodes at the bottom of the spark plug. The spark ignites the mixture.

The capacitor in the distributor draws off electricity that might otherwise cause a spark between the breaker points when they are in the open position. *See also* AUTOMOBILE; ENGINE. W.R.P./J.T.

Scuba stands for self-contained underwater breathing apparatus. A scuba diver (above) has a tank of compressed air on his back which supplies him with air through the mouthpiece attached to his face mask.

DIVING (dī′ ving) Diving is the way that people enter the underwater world. For thousands of years, people have explored oceans, lakes, and rivers by short dives beneath the surface. Today, underwater breathing devices allow people to stay beneath the surface for long periods of time.

For centuries, divers have been using breathing tubes. These allow divers to suck air from above the surface while they are submerged. Another method of staying underwater involves being lowered under the water in a watertight metal container. The trapped air inside the container allows the diver to breathe.

Both of these diving techniques are still used today. Breathing tubes, called snorkels, are popular with divers of all ages. Snorkels allow a person to breathe air while just below the water surface. Some improvements have been made on the watertight container method. The container, now called a diving bell, has compressed air pumped in from above the surface. The diving bell is of limited use because divers can reach objects below them but not above them.

Diving suits are used by some divers because they reduce the loss of body heat and allow the diver to stay underwater for longer periods. The helmet diving suit consists of a copper helmet attached to a waterproof suit. Air is pumped from the surface through a tube. Even though the diver wears weighted

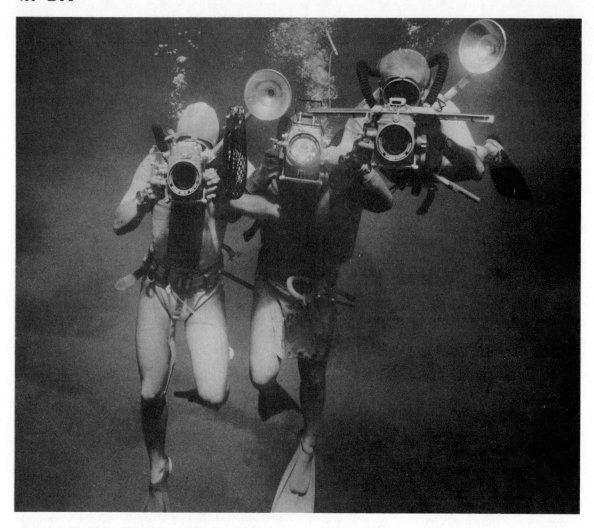

Special waterproof flashlights enable scuba divers (above) to explore dark levels of the sea. They can examine wrecks and study the ocean bed. They wear flippers on their feet to help swimming, and goggles so they can see clearly underwater.

boots to keep upright, movement is restricted and clumsy.

Scuba divers can spend the most time underwater. Scuba stands for self-contained underwater breathing apparatus. Scuba divers have a tank of compressed air on their backs and breathe the air through a mouthpiece. They also wear flippers on their feet to help swimming, and goggles so they can see clearly underwater. Aquanauts are scuba divers who work and live underwater.

Divers avoid coming up to the surface quickly because of a condition called the bends, or caisson disease. If a diver surfaces too quickly, the reduced water pressure causes nitrogen bubbles to form in his bloodstream. This results in horrible pain, paralysis, and sometimes death. By coming to the surface slowly, divers avoid this condition.

Divers do many important jobs. They are needed for the construction and repair of bridges. They study plant and animal life beneath the surface. They aid in finding drowned people. Military divers are very important during wartime. Diving is also a sport that almost everybody, regardless of age, can enjoy. *See also* BATHYSPHERE AND BATHYSCAPHE; COUSTEAU, JACQUES-YVES.

J.M.C./R.W.L.

DNA The initials DNA stand for deoxyribonucleic acid. DNA is the carrier of genetic information in cells. DNA is found in the chromosomes of cell nuclei and in certain cell organelles like the mitochondria and chloroplasts. DNA also occurs in some viruses. (*See* CELL; ORGANELLE.)

DNA is made of very long chains of units called nucleotides. Each nucleotide contains phosphate, a sugar called deoxyribose, and one of four organic, nitrogen-containing compounds called bases. Two kinds of bases are found in DNA: purines and pyrimidines. Two kinds of purine bases occur in DNA: adenine (A) and guanine (G). There are also two kinds of pyrimidine bases: cytosine (C) and thymine (T).

Two long chains of nucleotides coil around each other to form the DNA molecule. This coiled structure is known as a double helix. A double helix resembles a circular staircase or a twisted ladder. The sides of the DNA ladder consist of alternating sugar (deoxyribose) and phosphate molecules. Each "rung" of the DNA ladder consists of a purine base and a pyrimidine base connected by hydrogen bonds. The hydrogen bonds keep the double helix structure of DNA. (*See* HYDROGEN BOND.)

Only certain combinations of purine and pyrimidine bases may occur in DNA. Adenine (A) can combine with thymine (T), while guanine (G) can combine with cytosine (C). Any other combination does not work. Therefore, the rungs of the DNA ladder can be any of four combinations: A-T, C-G, T-A, and G-C. There are hundreds of these combinations in every gene. The order, or sequence, in which they appear on the double helix determines the genetic information of the cell. (*See* GENE; GENETICS.)

DNA can reproduce, or replicate, itself. In replication, the double helix uncoils. New purine and pyrimidine bases form hydrogen bonds with the appropriate bases on the original chains. Again, the only possible combina-tions are A-T, C-G, T-A, and G-C. In this way, two double-stranded DNA molecules are formed. The molecules then coil into the double helix structure. *See also* NUCLEIC ACID; RNA.   J.M.C./E.R.L.

DOCTOR (däk′ tər) A doctor is a person who has successfully completed an extensive program of advanced study at a college or university. The degree of "doctor" is the most advanced degree awarded in many fields such as philosophy (Ph.D.), law (LL.D.), religion (D.D.), education (D.Ed.), sci-ence (D.S.), and business administration (D.B.A.). In the medical fields, the major degrees are in medicine (M.D.), dental sur-gery (D.D.S.), dental medicine (D.M.D.), and veterinary medicine (D. V. M.), as well as more specialized degrees.

Most medical doctors have a four-year college education followed by four years in medical school. Medical school combines classroom instruction with practical learning experiences in hospitals and clinics. After graduation from medical school, a doctor spends at least one year as an intern under the supervision of experienced doctors. After completing an internship, the doctor may be-come a resident, concentrating on one specialized field. Although interns and resi-dents work with patients, they are considered to be in training and continuing their educa-tion. A resident becomes a certified specialist only after passing examinations given by spe-cialty boards in that field. Each state has spe-cific licensing requirements which must be met before a doctor can practice medicine in that state.

Medical doctors are either general prac-titioners or specialists. General practitioners treat many different ailments and must have general knowledge in many fields of medicine. If necessary, a general practitioner will refer a patient to a specialist. Specialists also have general medical knowledge, but they have completed a residency in a particular branch of medicine and usually limit their practices to that area.

Anesthesiologists control the use of anesthetics during surgical operations. Surgeons treat diseases by operations. (*See* SURGERY.) Dermatologists treat diseases of the skin. Internists treat diseases by nonsurgical methods. Neurologists use nonsurgical methods to treat diseases of the nervous system. Neurosurgeons treat diseases of the nervous system by surgery. Gynecologists treat diseases of the female reproductive system. Obstetricians care for women during and immediately after pregnancy. Ophthalmologists treat disorders of the eye. Orthopedic surgeons treat diseases of bones and joints. Pathologists study diseases and their causes. (*See* PATHOLOGY.) Pediatricians treat diseases in children. Psychiatrists treat mental disorders. (*See* PSYCHIATRY.) Radiologists use x-rays to diagnose and treat diseases. (*See* RADIOLOGY.) Urologists treat diseases of the male reproductive system as well as disorders of the kidney, bladder, and related structures.

As the amount of medical knowledge increases, there has been a trend toward specializing in one field of medicine. A relatively new specialty, family medicine, deals with the total health care of a patient and his or her family, regardless of their ages or ailments. Specialists in family medicine are much in demand in many rural and isolated areas. These specialists are gradually replacing general practitioners in many parts of the country. A.J.C./J.J.F.

DODO (dṓd'ō) The dodo (*Raphus cucullatus*) was a large, flightless bird that is now extinct. The dodo was about the size of a turkey and had a large beak, short legs, and small wings. It lived on the island of Mauritius in the Indian Ocean. Until European seamen arrived in the 1500s, the dodo had no enemies. Because it was so clumsy and had no fear, the dodo was easily captured and killed for food. Animals, such as dogs and rats, arrived with the seamen and destroyed most of the eggs. With no defenses, the dodo was soon endangered and by 1681 was extinct.

Portuguese sailors chose the name "dodo" because it means "silly." Because of the bird's slowness and general appearance, the word "dodo" has come to mean a dull-witted, slow-reacting person.

A.J.C./L.L.S.

DOG

The dog (dȯg) is an intelligent, carnivorous mammal that was probably the first animal to be domesticated. Dogs can be trained as hunters, guards, livestock herders, guides for blind people, and, most frequently, as companions and pets. The domesticated dog (*Canis familiaris*) of today probably descended mostly from the wolf (*Canis lupus*). Fossils show that dogs served as hunters for prehistoric people living 20,000 years ago.

Dogs were probably the first animals to be domesticated. The Afghan hound (above) is one of an ancient breed of dogs which were used to hunt foxes. Afghan hounds appeared in 3,000-year-old wall carvings at Balkh, a province in northern Afghanistan.

Breeds of dogs There are many different breeds of dogs. Some dogs, crossbreds, have

The Great Dane (above) is one of a breed of dogs that are tall, massive, powerful and have smooth coats. The Great Dane is a working dog. It was used to hunt boars since pre-Christian days. Working dogs serve as guards, livestock herders, and sled dogs.

parents of two different breeds. Others, mongrels or mutts, cannot be recognized as being from any particular breed. Purebreds are dogs with a father (*sire*) and a mother (*dam*) of the same breed. The American Kennel Club recognizes 124 pure breeds of dogs. These are divided into seven groups. Sporting dogs hunt by sniffing the air. These include pointers, setters, retrievers, and spaniels. Hounds hunt by sniffing the ground. Terriers hunt by digging in the ground, usually for rodents. Working dogs and herding dogs are the two most useful groups, serving as guards, livestock herders, and sled dogs. Toy dogs are small dogs raised as pets. Nonsporting dogs are larger than toy dogs, and are raised as pets.

Even the tamest dog has many of the instincts of its wild cousins and ancestors. There are several types of wild dogs which usually roam in packs. These include coyotes, dingoes, jackals, and wolves. It is possible to tame the puppies of most of these wild dogs.

It is difficult to make generalizations about dogs because they vary so widely in appearance and size. They range from the tiny Chihuahua which is 10 cm [4 in] tall at the shoulder and weighs 0.5 kg [1.1 lb], to the largest, the Irish wolfhound which is 90 cm [3 ft] tall at the shoulder, and to the heaviest, the St. Bernard, which weighs 100 kg [220 lb]. Most dogs have fur, but some are hairless. Most dogs have an outer coat of hair to protect them from snow and rain, and an inner, fluffy coat for warmth. The inner coat grows thick in the winter and is usually shed in the summer.

Most dogs have strong, muscular legs with five claws on the front paws and four claws on the hind paws. Puppies lose their 32 temporary teeth before they are six months

The Irish wolfhound and her pups (above) are sporting dogs bred to kill wolves. Irish wolfhounds are the world's tallest dogs.

old and grow 42 permanent teeth within the next few months. They have two fangs in each jaw and use these sharp, pointed teeth for tearing meat. A dog drinks by lapping liquid into its mouth with its tongue, a little at a time.

Dogs have weak eyes and are color-blind. (*See* COLOR BLINDNESS.) They rely mostly on their senses of smell and hearing. Dogs lick their noses to keep them moist; this helps them detect odors. Contrary to popular belief, a warm, dry nose does not mean the dog is sick. A dog can turn its ears to "catch" sounds which may be too faint for a human being to hear. A dog can hear sounds outside the human audible range, with frequencies as high as 30,000 Hz. (*See* HERTZ.) A dog's normal body temperature is 38°C [101°F]. Its heart beats irregularly, at 70 to 120 times per minute. When overheated or excited, a dog

pants in order to cool off its body. Although dogs rarely perspire, they do have sweat glands on their noses, feet, and skin.

A female dog mates only when she is in heat, a state of sexual readiness which lasts for about two weeks every six months. This is the only time a female dog can become pregnant. After mating, the female is pregnant for about two months before giving birth to a litter of 1 to 12 puppies. She then feeds her puppies milk for four or five weeks. Most dogs live to be 12 or 13 years old, though some live to be 18 or 20.

Since many dogs are abandoned or uncared for, humane societies urge dog owners to sterilize or neuter their pets to keep them from having unwanted puppies. (*See* STERILIZATION.) Male dogs are castrated (the testicles are removed) and female dogs are spayed (the ovaries are removed). These operations are permanent and cannot be reversed.

Diseases of dogs Dogs may suffer from many human diseases such as common colds and pneumonia. They may also suffer from mange, distemper, rabies, heartworm, worms, fleas, or ticks. Mange is a skin disease caused by a mite that burrows into the skin causing painful, itchy blisters. Distemper is a disease caused by a virus that affects the nervous system and the respiratory system. It is usually fatal. Rabies is also caused by a virus and affects the nervous system, causing insanity and death. A rabid dog becomes vicious and may bite people, causing them to get the disease if they do not get injections of anti-rabies serum. Vaccinations are available (and required in most states) to help dogs develop immunity to distemper and rabies. Heartworm disease is caused by a tiny, wormlike nematode that enters a dog's body in a mosquito bite. The nematode reproduces quickly and travels through the bloodstream, affecting the heart and lungs. Heartworm disease will cause death if not treated by a veterinarian. (*See* VETERINARY MEDICINE.) Worms affect almost all puppies. They enter a dog as larvae in its food. They cause vomiting and loss of weight, and should be treated by a veterinarian. Fleas and ticks are insect pests that cause itching and spread disease. Dogs frequently scratch or chew their skin until it is raw and bloody in an attempt to rid themselves of these pests. Fleas and ticks can be removed by using commercially available shampoos, powders, and sprays.

Aside from their value as pets and companions, dogs are often used in medical research. Insulin was discovered through experiments with dogs. (*See* DIABETES.) Ivan Pavlov, the Russian doctor, discovered the conditioned reflex by using dogs in his experiments. Various organizations called antivivisection leagues have formed to protest the use of dogs and other animals in research. They are primarily concerned that the animals may be treated cruelly during the experiments. The Society for the Prevention of Cruelty to Animals (SPCA) is active in enforcing strict standards of animal welfare. The SPCA and the humane societies offer low-cost sterilization of pets and enforce laws concerning abuse or mistreatment of animals. A.J.C./J.J.M.

Dogs have been bred for various purposes. The Irish setter (above) is a sporting breed developed in Ireland in the last 100 years. Irish setters are used to drive game into the open for hunters. Sporting dogs (pointers, setters, retrievers, and spaniels) hunt by sniffing the air.

DOGBANE FAMILY The dogbane (dȯg' bān') family includes about 1,000 dicotyledonous plants. (*See* DICOTYLEDON.) These plants often wind around other objects for support. (*See* MOVEMENT OF PLANTS.) Most dogbanes are tropical, though several species can be found in temperate areas of North America. Members of the dogbane family have large, funnel-shaped flowers that vary in color from pink to white to green. Many are poisonous, and have a bitter, milky fluid that discourages animals from eating the poisonous parts of the plant. One species produces a seed with enough poison to kill twenty people. Another species produces a sap which can be used to make rubber. A.J.C./M.H.S.

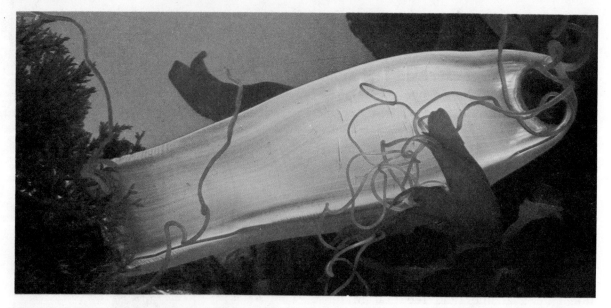

The dogfish lays eggs in a horny case known as a mermaids' purse. The dogfish is a small shark that is found in shallow, coastal waters in most oceans.

DOGFISH (dȯg′ fish′) A dogfish is a small shark that belongs to the family Squalidae. It is found in shallow, coastal waters in most oceans. There are eight species in North America. Dogfish grow to 1.2 m [4 ft] in length. They are slate gray above and pale gray to white below. Dogfish eat small fishes and invertebrates. Their skin is very rough.

S.R.G./E.C.M.

DOGWOOD (dȯ′ gwu̇d′) A dogwood is a small tree that belongs to the genus *Cornus*. It is a fast-growing, short-lived tree that is found in central and eastern North America. There are three species: the alternate-leaved dogwood, the flowering dogwood, and the roughleaf dogwood. The bright red berries that ripen in the fall are eaten by wildlife. The flowering dogwood has pink or white blossoms in the spring. It is a popular ornamental tree.

S.R.G./M.H.S.

DOLOMITE (dō′ lə mīt′) Dolomite is a mineral consisting of calcium carbonate and magnesium carbonate. Dolomite is the main source of the magnesium obtained from the earth's crust. Pure dolomite varies in shades from white to yellow. Impurities, such as manganese or iron, may give dolomite a pink or brown color. Because of its luster, dolomite is sometimes called pearl spar.

The term dolomite also refers to rock consisting chiefly of dolomite. Much dolomite rock contains fragments of fossils. Many mountain ranges in Europe, such as the Dolomite Alps, have great masses of dolomite rock. The rock also exists in various parts of the United States.

Dolomite is used in industry by iron and steel manufacturers. They use it in the smelting process. (*See* SMELTING.) Finely ground dolomite is used as a filler in rubber, putty, and paint. Marble made of dolomite crystals may have unusual colors. It is sometimes used as a building material.

J.J.A./R.H.

DOLPHIN (däl′ fən) The dolphin is a mammal that lives in all of the oceans and in some rivers. The dolphin feeds mainly on fish. Two of the commonest dolphins are the bottle-nosed dolphin and the common dolphin.

Bottle-nosed dolphins are the kind that can be seen in aquariums. They learn tricks that they perform for audiences, like leaping high into the air to get a piece of fish from the trainer's hand. They are extremely fast swimmers, and can make sharp turns and sudden stops. Other tricks include jumping through a hoop and retrieving a ball or some other object thrown by the trainer.

Scientists believe the dolphin is one of the most intelligent of animals. They rank its intelligence as equal to that of the chimpanzee. The bottle-nosed dolphin has sharp vision, excellent hearing, and a good sense of taste. It is different from other mammals in that it has no sense of smell.

The dolphin has a blowhole at the top of its head through which it breathes. As it blows air through its blowhole, it can make sounds that include whistles, clicks, and yelps. Scientists believe that dolphins communicate with each other by making these different sounds. People have tried to communicate with them, but have not been successful.

The bottle-nosed dolphin grows to 3.7 m [12 ft] in length, and weighs as much as 360 kg [800 lb]. The dolphin is grayish in color, and its back is darker than its belly.

Scientists believe dolphins (above) are among the most intelligent of animals. Dolphins are popular aquarium specimens because of their ability to learn and perform tricks. The common dolphin lives in warm ocean waters.

The common dolphin lives in warm ocean waters. It can grow to a length of 2.1 m [7 ft]. It weighs up to 68 kg [150 lb]. The common dolphin is black on its back and white underneath. It has gray and brown markings on its sides.

Large groups of common dolphins play around ships. For hundreds of years, sailors believed that their presence meant that the voyage would be a smooth one. P.G.C./J.J.M.

DOMINANCE (däm′ ə nəns) Dominance has three principal meanings in biology. In heredity, genes controlling inherited characteristics are received from both parents. A dominant characteristic shows up in the offspring if the gene for that characteristic is dominant. A dominant gene produces a dominant characteristic regardless of whether it is combined with another dominant gene or with a recessive gene. For example, the gene for brown eyes (B) is dominant over the recessive gene for blue eyes (b). A person with brown eyes can have either one or two dominant "brown eye" genes (BB or Bb). A person with blue eyes, however, must have two recessive "blue eye" genes (bb). An offspring from two blue-eyed parents will almost always have blue eyes because neither parent has the dominant "brown eye" gene. An offspring from two brown-eyed parents, or one brown-eyed and one blue-eyed parent, is likely to have brown eyes. (See GENETICS.)

In ecology, the dominant species in a particular community is the most prominent species, controlling to a great extent the other species there. For example, pine trees are dominant in many northern forests. Higher animals often establish dominance in a certain area, protecting their territory from any potential invaders. For example, a dog may establish its territory as its master's yard, and will attack squirrels or other invaders in its territory. It will not, however, bother animals in surrounding territories or yards.

Within a species, animals often fight to

establish leadership and a dominance hierarchy, or pecking order. In a dominance hierarchy, the dominants have their choice of food, mates, and shelter. The subordinates must accept whatever is left. Once the dominance hierarchy has been established, a subordinate rarely challenges a dominant. A dominance hierarchy helps reduce fighting within a group of animals of the same species, and helps set definite duties for each member of that group. Evolutionary change, or natural selection, is also a result of dominance. (*See* EVOLUTION.) According to the concept of survival of the fittest, when an environment cannot support large numbers of a given species, only the best specimens of that species, the dominants, will survive. A.J.C./E.R.L.

DONKEY (däng′ kē) The donkey (*Equus asinus*) is a horselike mammal that descended from the wild ass of Ethiopia and northern Africa. This small, surefooted animal stands about 1.2 m [4 ft] at the shoulder, and usually has gray hair. First trained several thousand years ago, the domesticated donkey is used for riding, carrying loads, or pulling carts. If mistreated, a donkey may become very stubborn, refusing to work or move.

The donkey is well-suited for hot, dry climates such as those in southern Europe and Asia, and northern Africa. Donkeys were first introduced into the United States in 1848. If a male donkey (jack) mates with a female horse, the offspring will be a mule. If a female donkey (jenny) mates with a male horse, the offspring will be a hinny. Burros are small donkeys often used as pack animals.

A.J.C./J.J.M.

DOPPLER EFFECT (däp′ lər i fekt′) The Doppler effect is the apparent change in frequency of sound, light, or radio waves caused by motion. For example, when an approaching train blows its whistle, the pitch of the whistle seems higher as the train comes toward you. The pitch seems to lower when the train passes and goes away from you. The actual pitch of the sound remains the same. The cause of this effect was first studied in 1842 by Christian Doppler, an Austrian physicist.

To understand the Doppler effect, it is necessary to know that sound travels in

The Doppler effect is illustrated below—sound waves from a moving train whistle are higher in pitch as the whistle nears a stationary observer.

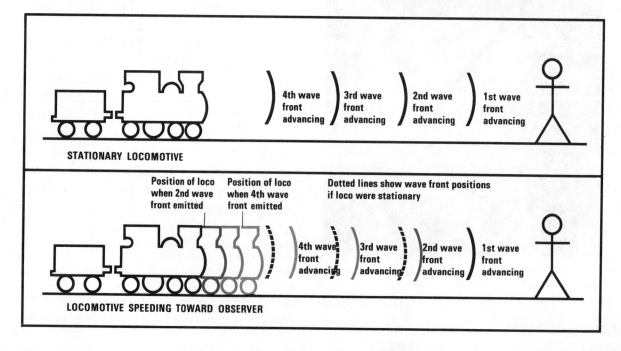

4th wave front advancing 3rd wave front advancing 2nd wave front advancing 1st wave front advancing

STATIONARY LOCOMOTIVE

Position of loco when 2nd wave front emitted Position of loco when 4th wave front emitted Dotted lines show wave front positions if loco were stationary

4th wave front advancing 3rd wave front advancing 2nd wave front advancing 1st wave front advancing

LOCOMOTIVE SPEEDING TOWARD OBSERVER

waves. The pitch of a sound depends on its frequency. The frequency is the number of sound waves striking the ear each second. When the source of sound is approaching, each wave sent out by the source has a shorter distance to travel than the wave that was sent out earlier. Each wave reaches the listener a little sooner than it would have if the source had not been moving. The waves seem to be more closely spaced. They have a higher frequency. As the train moves away, each wave starts a little farther away. Each wave seems to be longer than it would ordinarily be. The pitch is lowered.

The same thing happens with any other wave motion. Astronomers study the motion of a star by measuring the apparent change in the frequency of light waves due to motion. *See also* RADAR; RELATIVITY; SOUND; SPECTRUM. J.J.A./J.T.

DORMANCY (dȯr′ mən sē) Dormancy is a state of rest or inactivity in living things that is marked by greatly reduced metabolic activity. (*See* METABOLISM.) Dormancy usually occurs during or just before periods of unfavorable environmental conditions, such as a cold season. In temperate regions, most amphibians and reptiles, and many other animals become dormant or hibernate during the winter. (*See* HIBERNATION.) Most insects have a dormant stage in their development. (*See* METAMORPHOSIS.) Many shrubs and trees lose their leaves in the fall and remain dormant until the spring when new buds begin to form. (*See* DECIDUOUS TREE.) Many fruit trees require long periods of dormancy before they can bear fruit. Biennial and perennial herbaceous plants lose their stems in the fall, the roots remaining dormant through the winter. The seeds of many plants are dormant for several months until environmental conditions are favorable for germination. Some seeds have survived dormancies of more than 1,000 years. The delay in the growth of an embryo plant during its dormancy is called afterripen-

ing. Some bacteria and Protista form a thick, protective coat and remain inactive during unfavorable times.

If there is a sudden, unexpected and unusual change in environmental conditions, the dormancy of an organism may be broken. When conditions return to normal (unfavorable), the organism may not be able to survive. For example, if there is a mid-winter thaw, many trees will begin to form buds. When temperatures return to normal, sub-freezing levels, the buds will die. As a result, the trees will produce few, if any, leaves, and may not survive the following growing season.

A.J.C./R.J.B.

DORMOUSE (dȯr′ maȕs′) The dormouse is a small, bushy-tailed rodent. It is about 8 cm [3 in] long, and has large black eyes. Dormice feed mostly on seeds, fruit, and nuts. They live in Europe, Africa, and Asia. In the colder areas, the dormice hibernate through most of the winter. (*See* HIBERNATION.) J.M.C./R.J.B.

The fat dormouse (above) is found in Europe. It was considered a delicacy by the ancient Romans.

DOUGLAS FIR (dəg′ ləs fər′) The Douglas fir (*Pseudotsuga menziesii*) is one of the largest and most valuable conifers in the world. Native to western North America, this

The Douglas fir may reach a height of 100 m [330 ft] with a trunk 1.8 m [6 ft] in diameter.

member of the pine family may reach a height of 100 m [330 ft] with a trunk 1.8 m [6 ft] in diameter. It has flat needles about 2.5 cm [1in] long, and seed-filled cones about 10 cm [4 in] in diameter. The Douglas fir provides most of the lumber used in North America.

A.J.C./M.H.S.

DOVE AND PIGEON Doves (dəvz) and pigeons (pij′ ənz) are members of the same family, Columbidae. They have well-developed flight muscles, and are very similar in their ability to fly fast. They grow from 15 to 30 cm [6 to 12 in] in length, and can weigh from 28 to 255 gm [1 to 9 oz]. Doves are smaller than pigeons.

Doves and pigeons eat fruit and seeds. They feed their young with a milky secretion from the lining of the crop (saclike extension of the esophagus).

Doves and pigeons have always been a source of food for people. Certain types, like the carrier pigeon, have been trained to carry messages. Homing pigeons have been trained for racing and show. They can become a nuisance in large cities.   P.G.C./M.L.

DRAGONFLY (drag′ ən flī) The dragonflies are slender, long-bodied insects belonging to the order Odonata. The adult has

Pictured below are a fruit pigeon (left), a fantail pigeon (center), and a carrier pigeon (right).

four large, equal-sized, glassy wings with a network of supporting veins. The wingspread range of dragonflies is about 4 to 18 cm [1.5 to 7.2 in]. The head is large and is occupied almost entirely by compound eyes. The antennae are small, and the dragonfly relies mostly on sight to find prey. The dragonfly uses its long, thin legs as a basket to trap other small insects in midair. A dragonfly cannot walk, but is able to fly as fast as 100 km [60 mi] per hour.

After dragonflies mate in flight, the female deposits her eggs in the water or in aquatic plants. Within two weeks, the eggs hatch, releasing nymphs. Nymphs live in the water for as long as five years, breathing through gills, and capturing insects and small water animals with their long, hinged lower lips. The nymph matures into an adult through a series of 12 molts. (*See* METAMORPHOSIS; MOLTING.) The adult usually lives for only a few weeks.

Dragonflies are not harmful to people. They cannot bite or sting. They are helpful insects because they feed on mosquitos and other pests.   A.J.C./J.R.

A female aeshnid dragonfly (left) is pictured. The dragonfly's head is large and is occupied almost entirely by compound eyes. The dragonfly relies mostly on sight to find prey. Dragonflies are not harmful to people. They feed on mosquitos and other pests.

Dragonfly larvae (below) are found in ponds and streams, where they are fierce predators. They are equipped with a strong extendable "grabbing" organ, called the mask. A larva (left) shoots out its mask at a passing tadpole (middle). Another larva (right) rests with its mask retracted.

The *Metamorphosis of Narcissus*, a painting by Salvador Dali, represents a dreamlike situation.

DREAM (drēm) Dreams are activities of the mind when you are asleep. We say that dream experiences are imaginary, but they can be related to real experiences in the person's life. Some people say they do not dream, because they cannot recall anything about a dream. Others are able to remember their dreams in great detail. Dreams can be pleasurable, uneventful, or very frightening, like a child's nightmare.

Scientists have shown that almost everyone does dream, sometimes two or three times during each night. The scientists use a technique that involves recording eye movements of the person as he or she goes through the process of going to sleep, sleeping deeply, and waking up. During periods of dreaming, the person's eye movements become faster and move constantly as if they were following the action in the dream. These periods are called REM (Rapid Eye Movements) sleep. The REM usually lasts about 15 to 20 minutes. During REM periods, the pattern of the person's brain waves changes. (*See* ELECTROENCEPHALOGRAM.)

We do not know why we dream, but dreams seem to be important. Ancient peoples thought that dreams have meanings. People who dealt in magic claimed to be able to interpret the meaning of dreams. Some people believed that dreams could tell what would happen in the future.

Psychoanalysts, like Sigmund Freud, a famous Austrian doctor, studied dreams to understand why people have mental disorders. His method for treatment of neuroses, called psychoanalysis, is sometimes used today.

Some psychologists believe that dreaming is a period during which the brain "clears its registers" in preparation for the next day's conscious activities.   P.G.C./J.J.F.

DREDGING (drej′ ing) Dredging is the clearing out of silt, sediment, and other deposits from the bottoms of rivers and other bodies of water. Harbors and other waterways are constantly being clogged up. Mud and sand are carried into them by rivers or tidal waters. Harbors would become shallow if dredging were not carried out often to keep them deep enough so that ships could use them.

Dredging is also performed in the cutting of new waterways. Sometimes, when a waterway is being cut through rock, the material removed, known as spoil, is used for building. In land reclamation projects, material dredged from the sea is pumped ashore to build up the ground level. In the mining of alluvial deposits (such as sand formed by flowing water) by dredging, it is the material dredged up which is most important. (*See* GOLD.)

The machines that do this type of work are called dredges. Dredges move material underwater similar to the way that steam shovels do on land. Since the material dug out and other conditions affecting underwater excavation (digging and removing material) vary greatly, there are many different types of dredges.

The dipper dredge has a large scoop shovel called a dipper. The dipper is shaped like a box. It hangs on a chain from a long steel beam. The steel beam is called a derrick. The derrick is attached to a strong mast that can swing the derrick and dipper in a wide semicircle. By means of a chain being wound and unwound, the dipper can be raised and lowered. The derrick can also be raised and lowered.

When the dredging begins, the dipper is lowered to the bottom of the river or harbor. The derrick arm is swung in a semicircle to drag the dipper across the bottom. In this way, the dipper scoops up dirt and mud. Then the dipper is raised above the water and swung above a barge nearby. The bottom of the dipper has a door. The door is pulled open by a long cord to dump the dirt into the barge. Then the dipper is lowered again to dig more mud.

Grab dredges are used in deeper water than dipper dredges. Grab dredges have buckets that are shaped like big clam shells hinged at the top. Some have buckets shaped like the sections of a cut orange peel, all hinged together at the top. The buckets are attached to a long cable. When lowered to the bottom, the bucket is opened at the bottom, filled, closed, and then raised.

The ladder dredge has a series of buckets attached to an endless moving chain. The chain is supported by a long frame boom. The chain is kept moving by a powerful engine. As the buckets hit the bottom, they scrape up a load of material. When the buckets turn over at the top of the boom, they empty the material into a long chute. The chute carries the material to a place where it is discharged. A ladder dredge used on the Panama Canal had 40 buckets. Each bucket could lift 1.8 cu m [2 cu yd] of material from a depth of 15 m [50 ft]. The main use for this type of dredge is in mining gold and tin.

The hydraulic dredge, also called a suction dredge, is most useful for moving large amounts of beach or river sand. A suction pipe carries the sand and water to a pump. A discharge pipe leads from the pump to a barge or to a disposal area. Earth deposited by this process for dams, dikes, or building sites is called hydraulic fill. *See also* EXCAVATION.

J.J.A./R.W.L.

DRILLING (dril′ ing) Drilling is a process used for making holes in rock, metal, wood, plastic, or other materials. The tools used to make these holes are called drills or drilling tools.

The part of the drill that cuts the holes is called the bit. Most drills work by a spinning, or rotary, action. As the cutting bit of the drill rotates, it bites deeper into the material. Twist drills are a widely used type of drill. The hand drill sometimes used in the home workshop is a twist drill. The bit has two cutting edges at the tip. Spiral grooves, known as flutes, lead from the tip. The flutes allow cut material to pass back from the hole. Industry uses twist drills. They are inserted in machine tools called drill presses. Such drills are power-driven, either by compressed air or electric motors. The ordinary drill press has a platform similar to that of a butcher's scale. One or several drills are mounted above the platform. The operator pulls a lever to lower the drills to the metal placed on the platform. Some drill presses run automatically. They need an attendant only to supply material. These drills work at very high speeds. Their bits get hot. For this reason, bits are made of toughened steel or other hard, heat-resistant materials, such as tungsten carbide. Such materials keep a sharp cutting edge. Machine drilling bits are cooled and lubricated by cutting oils. The oils flow over the bits during drilling.

Boring is similar to drilling. But borers usually have only one cutting edge. Reaming is a process for making holes larger. Reamers may have straight or spiral cutting edges. Solid reamers come in various sizes to fit the hole being enlarged or finished. Expansion or adjustable reamers can be adjusted to fit the hole. Reamers are not used for making the first hole. Both boring and reaming processes use rotary bits.

The small portable power drill (left) can be used in the home. Drilling is a process used for a great number of purposes.

Carpenters use augers, which are drills with a screw in front of the cutting edge. The screw eases the cutting edge into the wood. Another type of auger, which is usually machine-driven, is used by geologists to take samples or cores of soil and soft rocks.

In drilling for petroleum, holes may be drilled thousands of meters through all kinds of layers of soft and hard rock. In the usual method of rotary drilling, a tough bit studded with diamond or with tooth rollers is rotated at the end of a long drill pipe. A drilling rig, called a derrick, up to 61 m [200 ft] in height, is needed to work with the long lengths of pipe that are used. At various times, drilling stops while another length of drill pipe is attached. Soon after drilling has begun, a larger pipe, called a casing, is sunk around the drill pipe to stop the hole from caving in. Watery mud is pumped up and down this casing pipe to cool the drilling bit. Rock chips in the mud are removed by filtering.

Offshore oil wells are drilled in a similar way, except that first a drilling platform must be anchored to the seafloor or tethered to float above the drilling site.

Rock drills, used for drilling shot holes in various mining operations, are usually run by compressed air that drives a chisel-shaped drill point. Some rock drills, such as those used to drill oil wells, have cutting edges like those on twist drills.

In certain modern machinery operations, holes are "drilled" without the use of a bit. High energy electron beams, and also high energy light beams from lasers, are sometimes used to make holes in very hard materials, such as diamond.

Drilling, as noted in the above paragraphs, is a process used for a vast number of purposes in fields ranging from carpentry and road building to oil drilling and dentistry.

J.J.A./R.W.L.

A South African gold miner (facing right) uses a compressed-air drill to cut into granite.

DROUGHT (draut) A drought is an extended period of dry weather. The extreme lack of rain during a drought causes serious damage to crops and livestock and increases greatly the danger of forest fires.

A severe drought may last several years. During this time, the dry soil may blow away like dust. Streams, ponds, and other bodies of water often dry up completely. Unless the land is irrigated, a severe drought can make it useless. (*See* IRRIGATION.)

The new ring that forms each year in trees provides an accurate record of annual rainfall. In a dry year, the ring is narrow, while in a wet year, the ring is wider. By studying these rings, scientists have determined that periods of drought alternate with periods of wet weather. Unfortunately, meteorologists (scientists who study the weather) are unable to predict accurately when a drought will begin. *See also* METEOROLOGY; WEATHER.

J.M.C./C.R.

DRUG

DRUG A drug (drəg) is any substance or mixture of substances other than food that can affect a living thing. Chemicals used as medication, alcohol, and substances such as marijuana are called drugs. Pharmacologists, the scientists who study drugs, consider all chemicals that affect living things to be drugs. Even the chemicals in automobile exhaust and other environmental pollutants are considered drugs. But the major portion of this article will concern itself with drugs used for medical purposes.

Drugs can prevent or cure disease. They also can relieve the symptoms or effects of disease, or change the workings of the body in some way. Hundreds of different drugs are available today. They may kill germs, relieve pain, stimulate the heart, calm the mind, help a person to sleep, or keep someone awake. Drugs are produced in various forms, such as capsules, tablets, liquids to be swallowed or injected, and ointments to be rubbed on the skin.

History Drugs have been in use for thousands of years. The oldest known written record of drug use is a clay tablet from the ancient Sumerian civilization in the Middle East. This tablet, made in the twenty-first century B.C., lists about a dozen drug prescriptions. It calls mostly for the use of plant materials.

The Romans opened the first drugstore and wrote the first prescriptions calling for definite amounts of drug ingredients. Although ancient people used many drugs, most of the remedies were useless. However, some drugs were effective. For example, the Greeks and Romans used opium to relieve pain. They took squill, another plant drug, to strengthen a weak heartbeat. The Egyptians used castor oil as a laxative. The Chinese ate liver to cure anemia.

During the 1500s and 1600s, scientists made important advances in pharmacology, which is the scientific study of drugs and their effects. These advances laid the foundation for later progress. In the early 1500s, minerals, such as compounds of lead and mercury, were used as drugs. Further progress of drugs depended on advances in knowledge of the structure and development of the human body. Although much medical progress took place during the 1600s, the role of germs as a cause of disease was not established until the 1800s.

The "drug revolution" started about 1800 and is still going on. The practice of medicine has changed greatly, in large part due to the use of drugs. Pharmacology has developed into an important science. The manufacture of drugs has become a large industry.

Scientists learned how to isolate (separate) drugs from the plants in the 1800s. In 1806, morphine became the first drug to be isolated. In the 1840s, the use of anesthetics during surgery was introduced. Later in the

1800s, Louis Pasteur, a French scientist, and Robert Koch, a German physician, established the germ theory of disease. Pasteur proved that germs cause infectious diseases, and that the spread of such diseases can be stopped by killing the germs responsible. Koch developed a method for finding out which bacteria cause particular diseases.

Important advances were made in the 1900s. In 1903, barbital, the first barbiturate, was introduced. In 1910, Paul Ehrlich, a German scientist, introduced chemotherapy. Chemotherapy is a method of treating infectious disease with chemicals. In 1922, Frederick Banting, a Canadian physician, discovered the hormone insulin, now used to treat diabetes. Six years later, Alexander Fleming discovered penicillin, the first antibiotic.

During the 1930s, amphetamines began to be used, chiefly to relieve depression. In 1935, Gerhard Domagk, a German physician, discovered the first sulfa drug, Prontosil.

In the 1950s, scientists developed several important synthetic, or artificial tranquilizers. These drugs came into widespread use. In 1960, birth control pills were introduced. (*See* CONTRACEPTION.)

The major efforts of drug researchers recently have been to find drugs that will help cure cancer and other diseases not yet conquered by medical science.

Types of drugs Drugs can be grouped in a number of different ways. They can be classified according to their form, such as a capsule, gas, or liquid. They can also be grouped according to the way they are taken or by their chemical structure. Pharmacologists generally classify drugs according to the helpful effect they have on the body. Classified in this way, many of the most important and widely used drugs fall into one of four groups.

The first group consists of the drugs that fight bacteria. The two main types of drugs that kill or aid the body in killing bacteria are

The leaves of the purple foxglove plant (above) contain the drug digitalin, used in treating heart ailments. This remedy is centuries old.

antibiotics and sulfa drugs. Doctors prescribe these drugs in treating meningitis, pneumonia, and many other infectious diseases. Large doses of penicillin or streptomycin kill bacteria.

The second group of drugs consists of drugs that prevent disease. These drugs include vaccines and antiserums and globulins. Some of the drugs, such as polio and smallpox vaccines, are very important because there is no known cure for the diseases they prevent.

Vaccines cause the body to produce substances, called antibodies, that fight a particular disease. The vaccine thus makes the body immune (resistant) to the disease. Unlike vaccines, antiserums and globulins contain antibodies rather than substances that cause the body to produce antibodies.

The third group of drugs, called cardiovascular drugs, are drugs that affect the heart and blood vessels. Doctors prescribe them in treating diseases of the heart and blood vessels. These diseases are the chief cause of death from disease in the United States. The three basic kinds of cardiovascular drugs are antiarrhythmics, cardiotonics, and vasodilators. Antiarrhythmics steady the heartbeat. Cardiotonics strengthen the heartbeat by causing the heart to beat more forcefully, therefore increasing the flow of blood. Vasodilators enlarge, or dilate, the blood vessels. Vasodilators also help in the treatment of hypertension, which involves high blood pressure.

The fourth group of drugs consists of the drugs that affect the nervous system. Five main types of drugs affect the nervous system. Analgesics relieve pain without deaden-

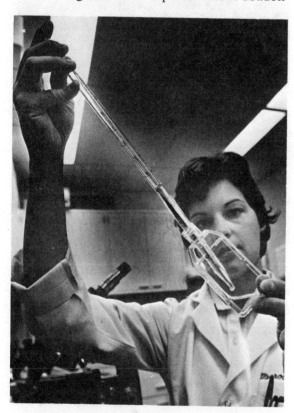

This research technologist is involved in the production of interferon, a drug now used experimentally to fight viruses and some forms of cancer but which could become a miracle drug in the future.

ing any of the other senses, such as touch or taste. For example, an analgesic such as aspirin may relieve a person's headache, but it does not prevent that person from tasting food. The two main kinds of analgesics are narcotics and nonnarcotics. Both kinds relieve pain, but narcotics also produce a dazed condition, and often a feeling of well-being. The most widely used narcotics are opiates and certain synthetic drugs. Opiates include codeine, heroin, and morphine. Doctors sometimes prescribe narcotics to relieve the pain of severe injury and some kinds of cancer. But overuse of narcotics leads to drug addiction, a condition in which a person has become so dependent on the drug that illness results if use of the drug is stopped. Drug addiction is discussed more fully later in this article.

Anesthetics are the second type of drugs that affect the nervous system. Anesthetics eliminate sensation. Dentists often give local anesthetics such as lidocaine. Local anesthetics affect feeling only in a certain area of the body. General anesthetics eliminate all sensation throughout the body, causing unconsciousness. These drugs are given to patients during surgical operations.

Hallucinogens cause a person to see, hear, or otherwise sense something that exists only in the mind. These drugs are also called psychedelic drugs. Hallucinogenic drugs include LSD, marijuana, and mescaline. (*See* HALLUCINATION.)

Stimulants fight sleep and tiredness. They increase the activity of the nervous system. Stimulants include caffeine, cocaine, and synthetic drugs known as amphetamines. Common names for amphetamines include "speed" and "uppers." Stimulants create a sense of well-being in most users, but many people become sad and uneasy as the effect of the stimulant wears off.

Depressants reduce tension and worry. These drugs decrease the activity of the nervous system. Tranquilizers calm a person without causing much drowsiness if taken in small enough doses. Sedatives, like tranquilizers, have a calming effect. But sedatives have greater ability to make a person sleepy.

Alcohol is the common name for ethyl alcohol, the drug found in alcoholic drinks. It relaxes most people and makes them drowsy. The use of alcohol, like the use of most drugs that depress the nervous system, may make a person dependent on it. (*See* ALCOHOLISM.)

People use many kinds of drugs other than those already mentioned. Diuretics increase the formation of urine. In certain diseases, the kidneys do not produce enough urine. Hormones are chemicals made by the glands of the body. The hormones control various bodily functions, such as growth and reproduction. Hormones are used to make oral contraceptives, which prevent pregnancy. These drugs work by interfering with the normal reproductive processes in a woman's body.

Vitamins are essential to good health. Such diseases as rickets or scurvy develop if a person has a vitamin deficiency. Antitumor drugs destroy cancer cells. Although many such drugs have been developed, they all attack normal cells as well as cancer cells. Scientists hope to develop drugs that will destroy only cancer cells.

Testing new drugs Before any new drug can be prescribed by doctors, it must pass many tests. These tests find out how effective the drug is. They also test the drug's safety. The first of these tests may be on laboratory animals, such as rats. The drug is also tested on pregnant animals to see if it damages the embryo before birth.

After the first group of tests, a few human volunteers take small doses while the substance's effects and side effects are noted. If it seems safe, a small group of patients take the drug to check on its effectiveness. This may be followed by clinical trials in which some patients receive the drug while others receive an inactive substance called a placebo. This is because a patient's knowledge that a new drug is being tested could affect the results of the trials. When the substance passes all these tests—involving thousands of people—it is licensed for general use by doctors. Sometimes, however, harmful side effects show up after many years of use, and the drug may have to be withdrawn.

Drug abuse and drug addiction Drug abuse is the harmful use of a drug. Many drugs can damage the body and the mind if taken for long periods of time or in large amounts. Most cases of drug abuse occur when people use drugs for nonmedical reasons. Commonly abused drugs include alcohol, hallucinogenic drugs, marijuana, nicotine (from cigarettes), opiates, sedatives, and stimulants. Many people use drugs to get a feeling of well-being. This feeling is often called a "high." Many people experiment with drugs out of curiosity, for a thrill, or because their friends use drugs. Much drug abuse results from feelings of loneliness, failure, or from other personal problems. Many drug abusers are people who easily become upset and cannot face their problems. The regular use of many drugs results in psychological dependence, which happens when the use of the drug becomes a hard-to-break habit. The regular use of some drugs can lead to a physical dependence, known as addiction.

Drug addiction is the inability of a person to control his or her use of a drug. Such a person is called a drug addict. Addicts' bodies depend on a drug so greatly that they suffer a painful illness if they stop using it. In addition, addicts also develop a tolerance to the drug. Doses that once satisfied a craving no longer do so. As a result, addicts need larger and larger doses to get the same effect.

Laws in the United States, Canada, and most other countries forbid the sale and use of heroin. Other narcotics and addicting sedatives can be obtained only with a doctor's prescription. But the strongest laws have not

This pharmacist is preparing a prescription.

eliminated either drug abuse or drug addiction. Other solutions to the problem must be sought.

Perhaps the best way to solve the problem of drug abuse is through early training and education in the proper use of drugs. Such educational programs have increased.

Rules of using drugs   No drug is absolutely safe. Improper use is harmful. Certain rules, if followed, prevent many problems with drugs. The rules are:

1. Do not take a drug prescribed for someone else. A drug that works for one person may not work for, or may be harmful to, someone else.

2. Do not save prescription drugs. A drug that may have cured a certain illness at one time may not work a second time.

3. Do not keep nonprescription drugs too long. All drugs change chemically in time.

4. Follow all instructions on drug labels. The label tells how much of a drug to take and how often.

5. Report unpleasant effects to the doctor.

6. Keep all drugs in a safe place away from children.

7. Do not take more than one prescription drug at a time without a doctor's recommendation. When taken together, some drugs can have unexpected side effects.

Drugs can bring tremendous benefits to people. They also present us with some of our worst problems. Drugs help cure and prevent many diseases. They also relieve pain and tension. But the misuse of drugs has led to addiction for millions of people.

The challenge that drugs offer lies in the discovery of medicines that may help cure cancer and other deadly disorders. Drug researchers continue in their efforts to find such cures.   J.J.A./J.J.F.

DRUMLIN (drəm′ lən) Drumlins are low, smooth hills formed by glacial movements. (*See* GLACIATION.) They range in height from 8 to 75 m [25 to 250 ft], and are usually 400 to 800 m [0.25 to 0.50 mi] long. The longest part of the hill is usually parallel to the direction of the ice flow.

Drumlins formed when the glaciers of the ice age moved across the land. The glaciers scooped up rock and other debris from the ground and deposited it elsewhere. These deposits formed drumlins. They often appear in clusters called drumlin fields. *See also* EROSION; ICE AGE.   J.M.C./W.R.S.

Drupes are fleshy fruits with single seeds, or stones. Typical drupes are shown above. The half cherry shows the drupe structure.

DRUPE (drüp) A drupe is a kind of fruit. Its seed is a single, stony pit. The seed is surrounded by juicy matter called the pulp, and is enclosed in a skin.

The best-known examples of the drupe are the plum, the cherry, the peach, and the apricot. Blackberries are made up of a number of small drupes called drupelets.

P.G.C./M.H.S.

DRY CLEANING (drī′ klēn′ ing) Dry cleaning is a process that removes dirt and stains from fabrics without the aid of water. Dry cleaning is not really ''dry.'' Liquids such as perchloroethylene, or other petroleum solvents, are used in the process.

Dry cleaning plants handle mostly clothing. Some of them also clean draperies and rugs. Many clothes, including most of those made of wool, must be dry-cleaned to prevent shrinkage, fading, or other damage. Some materials, like vinyls and artificial leathers, should not be dry-cleaned because the process causes them to crack and split. Most garments contain labels that tell how the fabric should be cleaned.

Dry cleaning began in France in the late 1800s. The process was called French cleaning when it was first introduced into the United States in the early 1900s.

In a dry cleaning plant, garments are cleaned with others of the same color and type. A worker called a pre-spotter removes stains that would become permanent in the dry cleaning process. The garments are then put into a special washing machine, which consists of a moveable drum filled with cleaning fluid. Special soaps, or detergents, are usually added to the fluid to help in the cleaning process. The drum rotates and the fluid flows through the garments removing dirt and stains. Afterward the clothes are put into an extractor, which spins them at high speed to remove the fluid. Some dry cleaning plants have machines that do both the washing and extracting in the same unit. After the extraction process, the garments are placed in a dryer. The garments are tumbled around inside a rotating drum filled with warm air. This dries the garments.

A worker called a spotter uses chemicals and a steam gun, if necessary, to remove any remaining stains. A steam gun is a small, gun-shaped device. It shoots a jet of live steam onto a stain or spot. The hot steam helps loosen the particles of dirt. Next, the garments go to the presser, or finisher, who uses steam-operated pressing and shaping equipment to restore the garment to its original shape. The garments are then inspected. Small repairs are made, if necessary. They are hung on hangers and covered with plastic bags.

Self-service dry cleaning became popular in the U.S. in the 1960s. Dry cleaning machines, activated by coins, automatically clean and dry the clothes. Some of these self-service stores have special equipment that can be used to remove wrinkles and bad stains. Self-service dry cleaning is less expensive than the professional process. However, some materials require special handling, which can only be done by professionals.

The dry cleaning industry is one of the largest service industries in the U.S. There are about 25,000 dry cleaning plants, employing more than 250,000 people. In addition, many thousands of laundries accept clothes for dry cleaning, and then send the clothes to a dry cleaning plant. There are about 25,000 self-service dry cleaning stores in the U.S.

W.R.P./J.M.

DUCK (dək) Ducks are water birds related to the geese and swans. Some live in fresh water, near rivers and lakes, and in prairie and mountain marshes. Others live in coastal waters.

Ducks have short legs, webbed feet, and flattened beaks called bills. Their legs and webbed feet serve as paddles. Some bills have rough edges which the duck uses for sifting food from the water and the mud, and for holding fish. The ducks with shorter bills use them to pry off snails from rocks, and to pull clams off the bottom of a lake or pond.

There are two main kinds of ducks: the surface feeders and the diving ducks. The surface feeders eat by up-ending themselves in the water and leaving their tails sticking out. The divers submerge and swim about under the water. Both are good flyers, once they get off the water and into the air. Surface feeders can fly directly into the air. Divers must flap across the water before they can become airborne.

The plumage of the duck consists of a layer of down feathers and a layer of waterproof feathers. The down is very fine and soft. It is next to the bird's skin and helps keep him warm. The outer feathers help keep the down layer dry. The outer feathers are covered with a waxy oil that comes from a gland at the base of the tail and is applied to the feathers with the bill. The male duck, called a drake, usually has brightly colored outer feathers. They are arranged in simple patterns, and include green, chestnut brown, blue, black, and white. The female, called simply a duck, has dull, plain feathers. She can hide easily when she is incubating her

SOME KINDS OF DUCKS

Common Eider Duck

Mallard

Common Shelduck

Carolina or Wood Duck

Shoveller Duck

eggs or taking care of her young ducklings. In the fall, ducks molt. The drake loses his bright feathers, and turns a brown color like the female. It is sometimes hard to realize that the male and female belong to the same species (*See* POLYMORPHISM.)

After molting, ducks migrate south to winter feeding grounds. They may use the same feeding grounds year after year. The drake and the female duck mate at their winter feeding areas. The new, colored feathers of the drake attract the female. Drakes are territorial, and drive away other males of the same species.

When the ducks migrate to the north during springtime, the male flies with his new mate. Very often, they return to the marsh where she was born. The ducks make a nest on the ground, in places like a clump of grass or a burrow. The female makes the nest. She lays from five to twelve eggs. When she starts to sit on the nest, the drake wanders away and does not help sit on the eggs. The ducklings are hatched in about a month. Most ducklings can run, swim, and find food the day they are hatched. They grow feathers and learn to fly in about five weeks.

Most ducks live in flocks during migration and at winter feeding grounds. You can see them in the fall flying in a "V" formation. One or two are at the pointed end of the V, and the rest form two lines trailing on both sides.

Wild ducks are protected by hunting laws and cannot be sold as food. Domestic ducks, the kind the farmer raises, can be sold in markets and are served in restaurants. The most common commercial ducks in the United States are the white Pekin ducks.

P.G.C./M.L.

DUCKWEED (dək′ wēd′) Duckweed is a family of 40 perennial aquatic plants that float on ponds in temperate regions. These monocotyledons are the smallest flowering plants known, producing flowers and fruits which are almost microscopic in size. The most common species, *Lemna minor,* has a green, leaflike frond with a tiny root growing into the water. (*See* VESTIGIAL ORGANS.) The frond produces either one stamen or one pistil.

Duckweed plants can double their numbers every 2½ days, and frequently they cover completely a stagnant body of water. Ducks and large goldfish feed on duckweed, helping to keep its growth under control. Duckweed is sometimes grown in home aquariums because it has a mild laxative effect on some tropical fish. Duckweed belongs to the same order as the arum family, and probably descended from the same ancestor as the palm family and the lily family. *See also* PLANT KINGDOM.

A.J.C./M.H.S.

DUCTILITY (dək′ til′ ə tē) Ductility is the capacity of certain solid substances to undergo permanent changes in shape without breaking. Soft metals, such as copper and gold, can be drawn out into wire finer than a human hair. Such metals are highly ductile. Ductility is a valuable property of many other metals, such as aluminum, iron, nickel, and silver. The term malleability is often used in place of ductility to describe the property of metals that allows them to be hammered into thin sheets.

Some metals are not in the least ductile. Cast iron, for example, fractures quickly when even slightly drawn out to greater length. Cast iron is termed a brittle metal.

Metals are not the only ductile substances. For example, modeling clay is a ductile, nonmetallic substance. J.J.A./A.D.

DUFAY, CHARLES *See* ELECTROSTATICS.

DUNE (dün) A dune is a hill or mound of sand made by the wind. Dunes are found in sandy regions, such as in deserts, along coastlines, and near large bodies of water. A large dune may be 150 to 180 m [500 to 600 ft] high, but most are much lower than that. Dunes usually

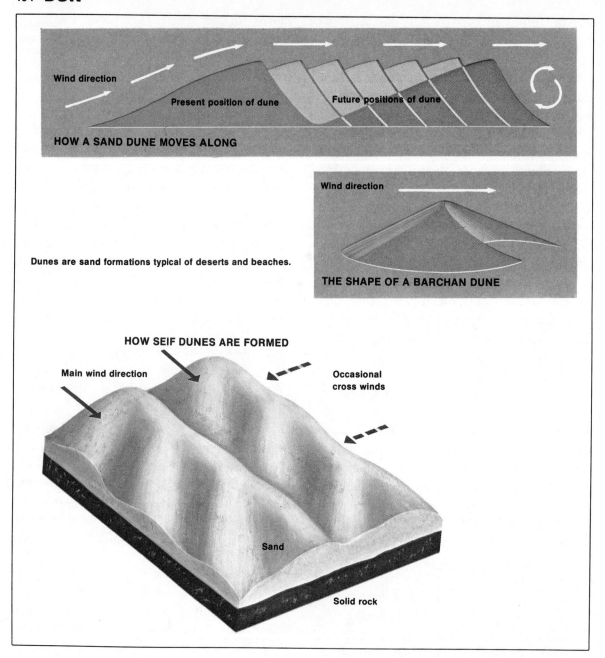

Wind direction

Present position of dune

Future positions of dune

HOW A SAND DUNE MOVES ALONG

Wind direction

THE SHAPE OF A BARCHAN DUNE

Dunes are sand formations typical of deserts and beaches.

HOW SEIF DUNES ARE FORMED

Main wind direction

Occasional cross winds

Sand

Solid rock

have a gentle slope on the side towards the wind, and steep slope on the side away from the wind. Crescent-shaped dunes are called barchan dunes. Seif dunes are long, steep-sided ridges of sand lying in the direction of the main wind movement.

A traveling dune may move across the desert. It loses sand on one side while it gains sand on the other. Some dunes make sounds when the grains of sand are blown by the wind. They are called singing dunes in some parts of the world. Dunes with unusual shapes can be found in Dunes State Park in Indiana. Other areas noted for sand dunes are Cape Cod in Massachusetts, the coastline of the Gulf of California, and the eastern shore of Lake Michigan.

Many ancient Egyptian cities and religious shrines were buried by sand dunes. Grass and trees are often planted to keep dunes from moving into farmlands and inhabited areas. W.R.P./W.R.S.

DUNG BEETLE (dəng′ bēt′ əl) Dung beetles are stocky beetles that use their shovel-shaped heads, broad, spiky legs, and paddlelike antennae to roll animal manure into balls. Each insect then buries its ball, feeding on the manure throughout the summer, and laying eggs early in the fall. The eggs develop into larvae which feed on the manure as they progress through the stages of metamorphosis. Dung beetles perform a valuable service. They help speed along the process of breaking down manure into nitrogen-containing compounds which can be used by other organisms. (*See* FOOD CHAIN; NITROGEN CYCLE.)

Dung beetles are oval, about 2 to 30 mm [.1 to 1.2 in] in length, with short, dark wing covers. In some species the male has an elaborate curved "horn" on its head which it uses to overturn other males. A dung beetle is able to consume more than its weight every 24 hours. There are 2,000 species of dung beetles. *See also* SCARAB. A.J.C./J.R.

DYE (dī) A dye is a chemical compound used to color materials. If properly applied, the shade of a dye is the same throughout the whole fabric.

Dyes are different from paints or stains. Paints and stains do not go much below the surface of a substance. Paint is worn and weathered away. Many stains can be removed with water and soap. A dye must be dissolved before it can work. In this sense, a dye almost becomes part of the fabric itself.

A brief history People have used dyes to color fabrics and other materials for more than 5,000 years. Dyers have also used mordants for several thousand years. A mordant is a substance used to hold the color to a fabric. Until the 1850s, the range of dyes was limited to a handful of dyes from animal and plant sources.

In 1856, William H. Perkin, a British chemist, made the first synthetic dye, called mauve, which is a pale, bluish purple. His starting material was aniline, then made from coal tar.

Until World War I, Germany was the largest producer of the world's dyes. Since then, the dye industry in the United States has grown rapidly. Today the United States' industries use about 8,000 different synthetic dyes.

Dyeing Textiles are placed in a dyebath, which is a dye solution. The textile fibers absorb the molecules of the dye. These molecules give the fibers the color. Dyed textiles vary widely in their ability to hold color. But all textiles are somewhat colorfast. Under normal use, a colorfast fabric does not change color. A fabric is lightfast if it does not fade in sunlight. It is washfast if it keeps its color after washing and drying. Some substances, such as chlorine bleach, may affect a fabric's color. (*See* CHLORINE.) Many dyes are not affected by such substances. Mordants are often added to dyebaths to make a substance more colorfast. Mordants combine with the dye molecules. Some chief mordants are tannic acid and soluble compounds of metals such as aluminum, chromium, copper, iron, and tin.

Textiles are dyed in different stages. If the fibers are dyed before being spun into a yarn, the process is called stock dyeing. In yarn dyeing, also called skein dyeing, the fibers are dyed after they are made into a yarn. Most stock and yarn dyeing takes place in large vats.

In piece dyeing, manufacturers apply the dyes after the yarn is made into cloth. Piece dyeing is used for many solid color fabrics. Some dyeing machines pull the cloth through the dyebath. Others operate by squeeze rolls. These rolls force the dye into the cloth.

Types of dyes The two main kinds of dyes are natural dyes and synthetic dyes. Synthetic dyes have replaced natural dyes in many instances. However, some natural dyes are

These are jet beck dyeing units. They dye fabrics under high pressure, which gives greater color uniformity and also saves water and energy.

still being used. Most natural dyes come from parts of plants, such as bark, berries, leaves, flowers, and roots. The madder plant, grown in Asia and Europe, once supplied bright red dyes for many fabrics, such as silk and linen. Saffron, a yellow dye obtained from the crocus plant, was used to dye silk and wool. Natural indigo, a blue dye, was obtained from the leaves of the indigo plant. Dyers used it on cotton, wool, and other fibers. This dye is still used on denim fabrics. Logwood is a dye which comes from a tree

that grows in Central America, Mexico, and the West Indies. Logwood is still used to supply black and brown dyes for cotton, fur, and silk. Henna, an orange brown dye obtained from a shrub of North Africa and the Middle East, was once used to color leather. It is still used in some countries to dye human hair.

There are nine basic kinds of synthetic dyes. Acid dyes are dissolved in acid solutions. These dyes give bright colors to nylon, silk, and wool. Basic dyes are so called because they are dissolved in alkaline solutions. Basic dyes are used on acrylic, wool, and other fibers. Direct dyes color material without the help of a mordant. They are used on cotton and rayon. Premetalized dyes contain metals that improve colorfastness. These dyes are often used on nylon, wool, and acrylic. Disperse dyes dissolve only slightly in water. Dyeing at high temperatures helps dissolve these dye particles into the fibers. Disperse dyes color acetate, acrylic, nylon, and polyester. Reactive dyes form a chemical bond with certain fabrics, including cotton and rayon. Sulfur dyes are dissolved in an alkaline solution. Fibers colored with such dyes are treated with oxygen to help fix the dyes. Vat dyes, processed in a way similar to the sulfur dyes, are among the most colorfast dyes. Sulfur and vat dyes are used chiefly on cotton and rayon.

Dyes contribute greatly to the wide variety of modern clothes and textiles. Dyes are also used by manufacturers in printing designs on fabrics. A machine applies different colors to various areas by means of screens or engraved rolls. This results in different and fascinating arrangements of color in many of the textiles today.   J.J.A./J.M.

DYNAMICS (dī nam′ iks) Dynamics is the branch of physics that is the study of movement. There are three very important laws in dynamics. They are called Newton's laws of motion, after Sir Isaac Newton. He was a very great English physicist who lived 300 years ago. He was the first person to codify these laws.

The first law of motion   An object usually stays where it is. It only moves if a force acts on it. When a body is moving it has a velocity. This velocity will only change if a force acts on the body. Imagine you are pushing a roller along a level piece of ground. If you stop rolling, the roller slows down and stops. This is because of the force of friction that acts

between the roller and the ground. So you must keep pushing the roller to keep it moving. You have to push with enough force to overcome the friction force. If you push the roller harder, you increase the force. Therefore its velocity increases.

The second law of motion   When a body speeds up or slows down, it accelerates. Acceleration is the rate of change of velocity. Suppose a body's velocity increases by two meters [6.5 ft] per second, every second. Then its acceleration is two meters per second per second. A force causes a body to accelerate. There is a simple relation between the size of the force acting on a body of constant mass and its acceleration. They are proportional to each other. If the force on a body is doubled, so is its acceleration. The acceleration also depends on the mass of the body. The larger the mass, the smaller the acceleration it will have for a particular force.

An example of this is when you hit a ball. When you do this you are putting a force on the ball. If you hit a ball twice as hard, it will go twice as far. Suppose the ball is twice as heavy. Then you have to hit it twice as hard to make it go the same distance.

The third law of motion   Every force creates a reaction. This reaction is as big as the force. It acts in the opposite direction. When your hand pushes on a table, the table is pushing back against your hand. Your pushing is called the action and the pushing up is the table's reaction. Without this reaction, your hand would push the table down. This does not seem like a law of motion. But it is. Without it, jet planes would not be able to fly. It is the reaction between the hot gases produced by the jet engine and the engine itself, that pushes the aircraft forward.

Moving in a circle   Imagine whirling a stone around on the end of a string. There is a force keeping it moving in a circle. This force

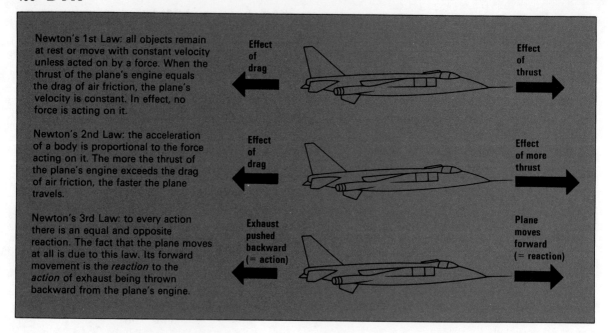

Newton's 1st Law: all objects remain at rest or move with constant velocity unless acted on by a force. When the thrust of the plane's engine equals the drag of air friction, the plane's velocity is constant. In effect, no force is acting on it.

Effect of drag

Effect of thrust

Newton's 2nd Law: the acceleration of a body is proportional to the force acting on it. The more the thrust of the plane's engine exceeds the drag of air friction, the faster the plane travels.

Effect of drag

Effect of more thrust

Newton's 3rd Law: to every action there is an equal and opposite reaction. The fact that the plane moves at all is due to this law. Its forward movement is the *reaction* to the *action* of exhaust being thrown backward from the plane's engine.

Exhaust pushed backward (= action)

Plane moves forward (= reaction)

is the tension in the string. It is the same with a spacecraft orbiting the earth. The force keeping it moving in a circle is gravity. This pull is called the centripetal force. According to Newton's laws of motion, a force produces an acceleration. These objects do not seem to be accelerating, but they are. Their speeds stay the same but the direction of their motion changes. This means that their velocities change. They are, in fact, accelerating. The stone is accelerating towards your hand and the spacecraft is accelerating towards the earth. But this acceleration is balanced by another one. This other acceleration tries to pull them away from the earth or your hand. So they stay as they are, going round in a circle.

Movement and energy All moving bodies have energy. This energy is called kinetic energy. The amount of it depends on the bodies' velocities and their masses. If a moving ball hits a still one, then the still ball moves. Some of the kinetic energy has been transferred to the still ball. But the total of the energy of motion of the two balls before and after the collision is the same. This is an example of the law of conservation of energy.

In practice, of course, a little of the energy of the moving ball will be lost as friction and in heating up the still ball when they collide. This is because the collision will not be completely elastic—that is, some of the kinetic energy will be absorbed by the balls themselves. There is another quantity that remains the same. It is called the momentum. The momentum of a body is its mass times its velocity. When two balls collide, some of the momentum is transferred. But the total momentum of the two balls remains the same. This is called the law of conservation of momentum.   M.E./J.T.

DYNE (dīn) The dyne is a unit of force in the centimeter-gram-second system. One dyne is equal to the force required to give a mass of one gram an acceleration of one centimeter per second per second.   J.M.C./J.T.

DYSENTERY (dis′ ən ter′ ē) Dysentery is a disease which affects the intestines, particularly the colon. The colon is the part of the large intestine extending from the cecum to the rectum. (*See* INTESTINES.) Dysentery usually includes inflammation of the colon with painful diarrhea. There are frequent movements containing blood and mucus. In some cases, fever and delirium, with a loss of consciousness, may develop. Two varieties of dysentery are amebic dysentery and bacillary dysentery.

A one-celled animal called an ameba causes amebic dysentery. This disease results in harsh inflammation of the colon and bloody diarrhea. Sometimes abscesses, which are swellings consisting of pus, form in the liver or brain. Amebic dysentery is usually spread by taking the amebas on food into the mouth. Fresh vegetables and fruits which have been frequently handled may be infected. The ameba at this time is in a resting, or dormant, stage called the cyst. As the cyst enters the intestines, however, it becomes very active. It grows and reproduces itself. (*See* ASEXUAL REPRODUCTION.) The organism causes the formation of holes, or ulcers, in the bowel. Ulcers may also form in the liver.

Amebic dysentery usually breaks out in warm and tropical countries. But it may also break out in cooler climates. For example, a frightening epidemic of amebic dysentery occurred in Chicago in 1933.

Ways to prevent amebic dysentery involve cleanliness, sanitation, and purification of water. In the treatment of this disease, certain drugs are used, such as emetine. The lack of symptoms does not indicate cure. Treatment should be continued until all amebas are destroyed.

Bacillary dysentery is caused by bacteria. This type of dysentery, quite common during the summer, occurs in all countries and climates. Bacillary dysentery occurs in institutions such as summer camps. The disease spreads by eating foods contaminated with bacteria. The symptoms, similar to amebic dysentery, include harsh, bloody diarrhea, cramps, fever, and loss of appetite. Bacillary dysentery can be prevented by cleanliness, sanitation, and the purification of water and food. Treatment includes a liquid diet and the use of antibiotics. J.J.A./J.J.F.

DYSPROSIUM (dis prō′ zē əm) Dysprosium is a metallic element. Its chemical symbol is Dy. It has an atomic number of 66 and an atomic weight of 162.5. It melts at about 1,400°C [2,552°F] and boils at about 2,300°C [4,172°F]. Dysprosium is one of the elements called the rare earths. It has seven isotopes. The metal has a valence of three. It forms salts of a yellowish green color. Dysprosium is found naturally in the minerals called gadolinite, fergusonite, euxenite, xenotime, and in other rare earth minerals. It was discovered by the French chemist, de Boisbaudran, in 1886. D.W./J.R.W.

EAGLE (ē′ gəl) Eagles are large birds of prey found throughout the world except in Antarctica. They have long symbolized power, freedom, and greatness. Among the largest eagles, the bald eagle (*Haliaetus leucocephalus*) and the golden eagle (*Aquila chrysaetos*) grow to a length of 90 cm [36 in], weigh 6 kg [13 lb], and have a wingspan of 2 m [6.6 ft]. As with most birds of prey, the female is larger than the male.

Eagles have large heads, with large, very keen eyes. They have rectangular wings which they use to soar gracefully through the air in search of food. The beak is strong, about 5 cm [2 in] long, the upper part curving over the lower part and ending in a sharp point. The legs and feet are very strong, and the toes end in sharp, clawlike talons. Eagles are aggressive predators, hunting during the day by swooping down on prey, grabbing it and killing it with their talons. Eagles are carnivores and usually eat rodents and small animals, though some eagles prey on larger animals such as chamois, goats, and livestock weighing as much as 10 kg [22 lb].

An eagle usually makes a nest, or aerie, in

The Chinese serpent eagle (facing left) lives in tall forest treetops.

the top of a tall tree. One nest usually serves an eagle for its entire life (20 to 50 years) and may be as deep as 6 m [20 ft] and as wide as 3 m [10 ft]. Eagles begin to mate in the spring of their fourth year and keep the same mates for life. At breeding time, a pair of eagles establishes its territory and prevents all other eagles from entering. (*See* DOMINANCE.) The female lays one or two large eggs 8 cm [3 in] long, weighing 150 g [5.4 oz], and stays with them for 35 to 45 days until they hatch. During this time, the male brings food to the female in the nest. If there are two eggs, the eaglet which hatches first is usually larger, and it kills the other eaglet.

Of the 48 different kinds of eagles, only the bald eagle and the golden eagle are native to North America. Others, such as the serpent eagles, harpy eagles, monkey-eating eagles, and sea eagles, live in widely varied parts of the world. Because eagles sometimes prey on livestock, they are often hunted by ranchers and farmers. Eagles in many parts of the world (including the United States) face extinction from hunting and from poisoning by insecticides and pesticides. Many countries have established laws to protect eagles. *See also* BIRD; CONSERVATION.   A.J.C./M.L.

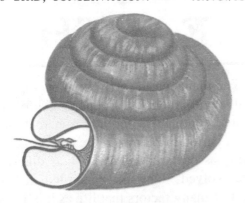

The cochlea, a part of the inner ear, transforms sound vibrations into nerve impulses.

EAR (ir) The ear is the organ of hearing. With our ears, we hear all sound coming from out-

side the body. The ear also has a special part that lets us keep our balance. Because we have two ears, we are able to locate sounds in space. We learn to talk by imitating speech sounds reaching us through the ear. Our ears are of primary importance in the process of exchanging ideas and thoughts with other people.

The ear is a complicated and sensitive organ. It changes the vibration of air patterns into electrical signals that reach the brain. It is divided into three parts for the purpose of studying and understanding its action. These parts are the outer ear, the middle ear, and the inner ear.

The outer ear is the fleshy part on the outside of the head. It is called the auricle or pinna. Its main function is to collect sound waves so that they can travel along the external auditory canal to the middle ear. In humans, the pinna lies close to the head, and cannot move around. Certain animals, including the horse, the dog, and the cat, can move their pinnae around to gather sounds more efficiently.

The external auditory canal is about 2.5 cm [1 in] in length, and ends at the tympanic membrane. The tympanic membrane is a thin sheet of tissue about 6 mm [0.25 in] across. Sound waves reaching the tympanic membrane cause it to vibrate, and pass the waves on to the middle ear. The external auditory canal is lined with fine hairs and with very small glands that produce wax. The hairs and wax protect the ear by keeping out dust and small insects.

The middle ear begins with the inner side of the tympanic membrane and ends at another membrane, called the oval window. Within the middle ear are three small bones. The first, called the malleus, is attached to the inner surface of the tympanic membrane. The malleus is then hinged to the incus. Finally, the incus connects to the stapes which is attached to the membrane of the oval window. These three bones, being hinged as they are,

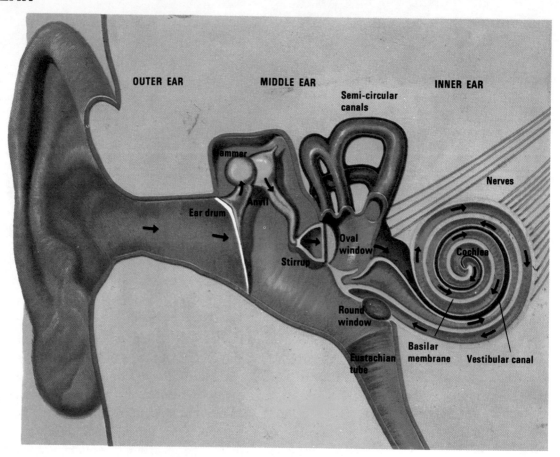

In this cross section, the arrows show the direction of air and mechanical vibrations in the ear.

can move freely and transmit sound waves to the inner ear.

The inner ear contains the cochlea. The cochlea is a cavity in the temporal bone of the skull and has a spiral shape. Sound waves reach the inner ear by vibrations of the oval window membrane. The cochlea is filled with a fluid and a thin length of tissue called the basilar membrane. Attached to this is the sense organ for hearing, the organ of Corti. The organ of Corti contains many tiny hair cells that respond to sound waves. The sound vibrations are changed into nerve impulses which are sent along to the brain through the auditory nerve.

The air pressure on either side of the tympanic membrane must be equalized so that the membrane can vibrate freely. Air can get to the middle ear side of the tympanic membrane through a narrow tube, called the eustachian tube, which is connected with the back of the throat. Hearing can be disturbed if this tube becomes clogged when a person has a cold.

P.G.C./J.J.F.

EARTH

The planet earth (ərth) has developed an ideal environment for supporting life. The oceans, continents, and atmosphere formed over a period of billions of years. Organisms as tiny as bacteria and as large as dinosaurs have evolved, flourished, and died. It is the result of many factors that life as it is known today evolved. (*See* EVOLUTION.)

The earth and the universe The earth is the third planet from the sun. Of the nine

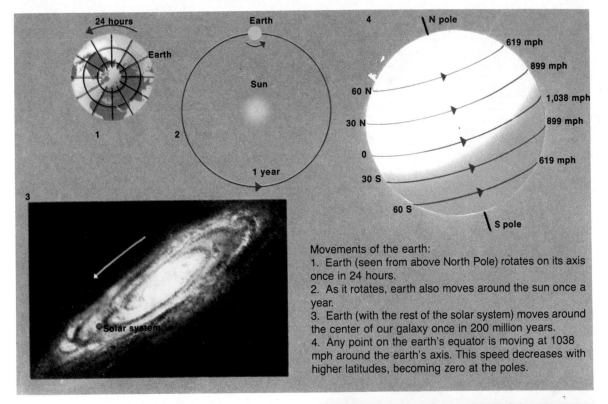

Movements of the earth:
1. Earth (seen from above North Pole) rotates on its axis once in 24 hours.
2. As it rotates, earth also moves around the sun once a year.
3. Earth (with the rest of the solar system) moves around the center of our galaxy once in 200 million years.
4. Any point on the earth's equator is moving at 1038 mph around the earth's axis. This speed decreases with higher latitudes, becoming zero at the poles.

planets, it is the fifth largest. The earth has a diameter of almost 13,000 km [8,000 mi], and a surface area of about 500,000,000 sq km [200,000,000 sq mi]. Water covers about 70% of the surface area.

The earth is always moving in four ways. It spins on its axis, causing day and night. It takes the earth slightly less than one day (24 hours) to make a complete turn. The earth also revolves around the sun, taking about one year for a complete revolution. The axis of the earth also shifts or wobbles like that of a spinning top beginning to slow down. Finally, with the rest of the solar system, the earth swings around the center of the Milky Way galaxy. This trip takes about 200 million years.

The earth spins on an axis which is tilted at 23½° toward a line perpendicular (at a right angle) to its path around the sun. The movement of the earth around the sun and the tilt of the earth's axis cause the seasons.

The nine known planets of the solar system are held to their orbits around the sun by

THE EARTH

Diameter: 12,756 km [7,926 mi] at equator

Circumference: 40,074 km [24,901 mi] at equator

Surface temperature:
minimum recorded: −88°C [−127°F]
maximum recorded: 58°C [136°F]

Gases in the Atmosphere:
nitrogen 78.09%
oxygen 20.95%
argon 0.93%
carbon dioxide and others in small quantities

Composition of the Earth's crust:
oxygen 46.60%
silicon 27.72%
aluminum 8.13%
iron 5%
calcium 3.63%
sodium 2.83%
potassium 2.59%
others 1.41%

the force of gravity. Gravity also holds the moon in orbit around the earth. The tides are caused by gravity. The highest tides occur when the earth, the moon, and the sun are in a straight line.

The earth's crust changes gradually—by erosion, or suddenly and violently, through earthquakes and volcanic eruptions. Mount Etna (above), an active volcano on the coast of Sicily, was photographed at night. The height and crater dimensions of Mount Etna are subject to constant change.

Earth zones   The earth is divided into three main zones: the atmosphere, the hydrosphere, and the lithosphere. The atmosphere is like a gas envelope surrounding the earth. It provides the air necessary for life, and protects the earth from extreme heat and cold. Physi-cal changes in the atmosphere are responsible for the weather. A large percentage of the oxygen in the atmosphere comes from photo-synthetic plants. (*See* PHOTOSYNTHESIS.)

The hydrosphere consists of the water and ice on earth. Water is essential for all life on earth. The lithosphere consists of the rocks that form the earth's crust. The three types of rocks found in the earth's crust are classified by how they were formed. They are: igneous rock, metamorphic rock, and sedimentary

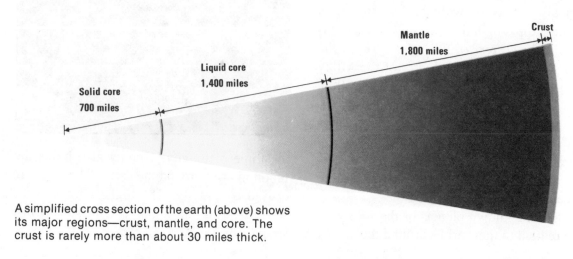

Solid core
700 miles

Liquid core
1,400 miles

Mantle
1,800 miles

Crust

A simplified cross section of the earth (above) shows its major regions—crust, mantle, and core. The crust is rarely more than about 30 miles thick.

The continent of Africa, with the dry Sahara desert in the north, is visible in this photograph of the earth which was taken from space. Such pictures give scientists information about our planet which cannot be obtained on the surface.

rock. The earth's crust varies in thickness from 8 km [5 mi] under the oceans to about 32 km [20 mi] under the continents. Beneath the crust is the mantle, which is about 2,900 km [1,800 mi] thick. Mantle rocks are far more dense than those of the crust. (*See* DENSITY.) Within the mantle is the earth's core. It is thought to be solid at the center, but surrounded by a liquid envelope.

The age and history of the earth   Not long ago, most people believed that the earth was formed recently. Many thought the earth was created in 4004 B.C., a date fixed by generations of people listed in the Bible.

Today, it is generally accepted that the earth formed billions of years ago, possibly from a vast cloud of dust and gases. (*See* COSMOLOGY.)

By studying fossils, scientists have been able to unravel some of the story of life on earth. Methods have been developed that can determine the age of fossils and rocks. (*See* DATING.) Scientists estimate the earth to be about 4.5 billion years old.

The history of the earth is divided into four main time periods: the Precambrian era, the Paleozoic era, the Mesozoic era, and the Cenozoic era. The Precambrian era covers the first 4 billion years of the earth. During this time, the crust of the earth melted and cooled, and many elements were formed. Some primitive organisms lived in the seas about one billion years ago, but before them there are no fossils of living things.

The Paleozoic era began 600 million years ago and lasted about 375 million years. Algae were plentiful, and reptiles, amphibians, and fish became common. Plant life flourished. The Paleozoic era also saw the formation of the Appalachian Mountains.

The Mesozoic era began about 225 million years ago and lasted 160 million years. This was the age of dinosaurs. Cone-bearing plants (conifers) became common, as did insects. Birds and mammals appeared for the first time.

The Cenozoic era started 65 million years ago and extends to the present. During this time, the ice ages occurred. The huge glaciers that moved across the continents had a great effect on the landscape of the earth. Mammals became the dominant land creatures. Flowering plants flourished. The Alps, Himalayas, and Rocky Mountains formed during this period. Perhaps the most important event of the Cenozoic era has been the evolution of humans which occured relatively recently. *See also* ASTRONOMY; GEOLOGICAL TIME SCALE.   J.M.C./W.R.S.

An earthquake in 1906 caused great damage (above) in San Francisco.

EARTHQUAKE (ərth′ kwāk′) An earthquake is a movement of the earth's crust that causes the ground to shake or vibrate. Of the thousands of earthquakes that occur each year, only a few are felt or cause major damage. The most destructive earthquakes are those that occur near cities or other populated areas. Most casualties associated with earth-

quakes are caused by buildings or other artificial structures collapsing. However, when an earthquake occurs in a large city, fire is frequently one of the major causes of damage.

Earthquakes are detected by sensitive instruments called seismographs. (*See* SEISMOLOGY.) The strength of an earthquake is measured on the open-end Richter Scale.

Powerful earthquakes may cause huge sea waves called tsunamis. These waves cause heavy damage when they hit the coastline. Fires often spread in an area hit by an earthquake because of broken gas lines and electrical short circuits. For example, in the San Francisco earthquake of 1906, three-fourths of the damage to the city was by fire.

Earthquake zones There are two main earthquake zones: the circum-Pacific belt and the Alpide belt. The circum-Pacific belt, often called the ring of fire, includes the mountain ranges and islands surrounding the Pacific Ocean. The Alpide belt extends across southern Europe and Asia. Other earthquakes occur beneath the oceans along the mid-oceanic ridges.

Cause of earthquakes The earth's crust is made up of about 20 plates that are always moving and rubbing against each other. When the edges of two plates become jammed, tension builds up. The tension is relieved by a sudden movement of the plates, causing an earthquake. Sometimes one plate is forced beneath the other to cause an earthquake.

As tension between two plates builds up, large amounts of energy also build up. When the force finally is released in an earthquake, it is transmitted to the surrounding areas in two waves. The first is the compression, or primary, wave. It acts like a sound wave and creates a rumble or muted boom. This may be people's first warning that a quake is coming.

The secondary, or shear, wave follows. This is the wave that can cause damage. It

This church in southern Italy was almost completely destroyed by an earthquake.

passes through solids of the earth's crust, moving and shaking things at the surface.

The San Andreas fault in western California is thought to be the edge between two plates. In 1906, it shifted, causing the San Francisco earthquake. Seismologists (scientists who study earthquakes) predict that a major earthquake may occur along the San Andreas fault in the next 50 to 100 years.

Other fault lines which could result in earthquakes in the United States are in Hawaii, Missouri, New Jersey, and New England. A series of quakes in 1811-12 in the town of New Madrid, Missouri, may have been the worst in American history. The first quake was felt as far away as Boston, Massachusetts. The series raised about 65 sq km [25 sq mi] of ground 6 m [20 ft]. It caused a new lake to form, and it made the Mississippi River run backwards for a time.

Scientists now generally agree on what causes earthquakes and where they are most likely to occur. When they will happen is still a matter of continuing research. Accurate forecasts could save many lives.

A number of successful predictions have been made. The most notable was in China in February 1975. Because of the advance warning, officials evacuated people and animals to open ground, and thousands of lives were saved in the severe earthquake which followed.

One of the indicators of the Chinese quake was the strange behavior of animals. Once thought to be merely folk lore, scientists are now studying this aspect of prediction seriously. Many now believe that animals are more sensitive than humans to physical changes that are known to precede a quake. These changes include a shift in the angle or height of ground surfaces, ionization of the air due to the electricity produced by internal pressures, the presence of radon gas, vibrations, shifts in the earth's magnetic field, and the rise or fall of ground water.

Advanced electronic surveying methods using laser beams enable scientists to measure the rate at which the earth's crust is moving. In an area south of San Jose, California, they were able to determine that points on either

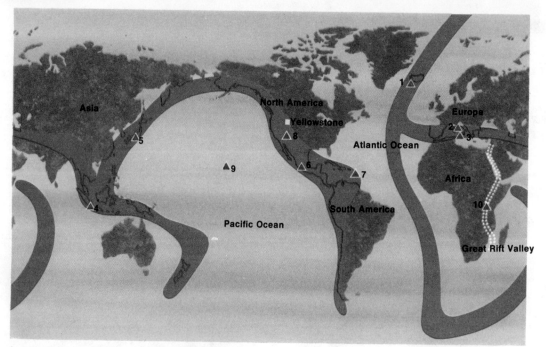

A map (above) of the world's earthquake-prone regions shows that most quakes occur in two great belts of the earth's surface.

side of the San Andreas fault were moving toward each other at a rate of about 9 cm [3.5 in] per year.

Surveillance by such methods, and the measure of radon gas released in fault areas, seem to offer the most hope that scientists will be able to forecast quakes with great accuracy. *See also* CONTINENTAL DRIFT; PLATE TECTONICS.   J.M.C./W.R.S.

EARTHWORM (ərth′ wərm′) An earthworm is any of 1,800 species of segmented worms belonging to the phylum Annelida. The most common earthworm, *Lumbricus terrestris,* is found in moist soil in temperate regions throughout the world. Earthworms vary in size from 1 mm [0.04 in] to 3.3 m [11 ft]. The earthworm has a very primitive brain, allowing it to respond to heat, light, or touch, but it has no sense organs. Each segment, or annulus, except the first and last, has four pairs of stiff bristles called setae. The setae are made of chitin, and are used for movement.

The earthworm has a complete digestive system. (*See* DIGESTION.) Its alimentary canal runs the entire length of its body with a mouth in the first segment and an anus in the last. As the earthworm moves, it swallows the soil along with any digestible decaying plant matter contained in it. (*See* HUMUS.) Gardeners and farmers consider the earthworm an important animal. As it ''eats'' the soil, it leaves air spaces needed by the roots to grow. The earthworm moves by stretching out its front part, grabbing onto the soil with its setae, then pulling up its rear part. In order to do this, the earthworm has evolved two sets of muscles. Circular muscles surround each segment and can make the worm thinner or fatter. Longitudinal muscles extend the length of the worm and can shorten or lengthen the body.

The earthworm has excretory structures called nephridia in each segment. (*See* EXCRETION.) It has five, heartlike aortic arches that pump hemoglobin-containing blood through two major blood vessels. The earthworm breathes through its skin. Air between particles of soil diffuses across the smooth, moist skin into the blood. (*See* DIFFUSION.) When it rains, these air spaces become filled with water and the earthworm will drown unless it comes to the surface. If the weather is too hot and dry, the earthworm's skin loses some of its moisture, and air cannot diffuse into the worm as easily. This often results in the death of the earthworm.

Earthworms are hermaphrodites, meaning they have both male and female reproductive structures. (*See* REPRODUCTION.) They cannot fertilize themselves, however. (*See* FERTILIZATION.) During mating, the clitellum secretes a mucuslike fluid which surrounds both worms. The clitellum is a swollen band around the worm between segments 32 and 37. After sperm are exchanged, the earthworms move away from each other. A few days later the fertilized eggs are wrapped up in a cocoon produced by the clitellum. Small earthworms emerge from the cocoon within a month. They become sexually mature within three months, and reach full size within a year.

Because earthworms often come to the surface at night when their natural enemies, the birds, are not hunting, they are sometimes called night crawlers. They are also called angleworms because they are often used as bait by fishermen.   A.J.C./C.S.H.

EARWIG (ir′ wig) An earwig is any of 1,200 species of insects belonging to the order Dermaptera, and characterized by pincers at the rear of the body. These pincers are used to capture prey, or used for defense, for fighting for a mate, or to help fold up the hindwings. Earwigs also have a pair of thin, membranous hindwings covered by leathery forewings. Some species, however, are wingless or have vestigial wings. (*See* VESTIGIAL ORGANS.)

Earwigs have flat, long, brownish bodies ranging in length from 0.6 to 5.0 cm [0.25 to 2.0 in]. They live in dark, moist places such as in decaying plant matter or under stones. Most species are tropical; there are less than 20 kinds in the United States. These nocturnal insects are omnivores, feeding on both plant and animal matter. Though some earwigs cause damage to fruits and flowers, many also eat pests such as caterpillars, slugs, snails, and thrips.

One worldwide species of earwig is able to defend itself by squirting a foul-smelling liquid from a special gland in the abdomen. Other types of earwigs are parasites on rodents and bats. Earwigs get their name from the superstition that they enter a sleeping person's ear.   A.J.C./J.R.

EASTMAN, GEORGE (1854--1932) George Eastman (ēst′ mən) was an American manufacturer and inventor. He made it possible for millions of Americans to become amateur photographers. Early cameras were expensive and bulky, and the developing process was complicated. In 1879, Eastman invented a machine for coating the glass plates used to receive images in cameras. Up to then, the process had been done by hand.

In 1884, he introduced an inexpensive roll film that had a paper base, and a roll holder for winding the film in the camera. The big breakthrough came in 1888. Eastman founded the Eastman Kodak Company in Rochester, New York, and introduced a small, light camera called the Kodak. Kodaks sold for $25, and thousands of people bought them. In 1900, Eastman came out with a $1 model. It sold in the millions, and created a tremendous boom in amateur photography in the United States.

Eastman donated over $100 million to schools and charities. He founded the well-known Eastman School of Music in Rochester. His home in Rochester is now a photography museum. *See also* CAMERA; PHOTOGRAPHY.   W.R.P./D.G.F.

EBONY (eb′ ə nē) Ebony is a very hard wood from a tree of the genus *Diospyros*. Ebony trees grow mainly in Japan, the Philippines, India, Sri Lanka, Africa, and North and South America.

The outer wood, called sapwood, is white and often tinged with a gray or pink shade.

The inner wood, called heartwood, is dark brown or black. A hard gum fills the heartwood fibers. This gum probably adds to the property of ebony which makes the wood easy to work and carve. Ebony is used mainly for black piano keys, flutes, knife and brush handles, cabinets, and furniture.

The persimmon trees of the United States and the Orient are a type of ebony. These trees, having very little black heartwood, are of no commercial value. The hard sapwood of the American persimmon is used to make wooden heads for golf clubs.   J.J.A./M.H.S.

ECHIDNA (i kid′ nə) The echidna (*Tachyglossus aculeatus*) is one of only two kinds of primitive, egg-laying mammals or monotremes. (*See* PLATYPUS.) It is native to Australia, New Guinea, and Tasmania. The echidna may reach a length of 78 cm [31 in]. It has a thin, beaklike nose and mouth. Its body is covered with long, dark hair and sharp spines. The echidna has short legs and long, sharp claws which it uses for digging. If threatened, an echidna may roll up in a ball, exposing its spines to an enemy, or it may burrow into the ground for protection.

The echidna feeds at night by digging into ant or termite nests and licking up the insects with its long, sticky tongue. (*See* NOCTURNAL HABIT.) Because of its diet and appearance, the echidna is often called the spiny anteater. The female lays one egg which she keeps in a pouch on her belly. This pouch, similar to that of the marsupials, develops only during the mating season. After the egg hatches, the young echidna stays in the pouch for several weeks, feeding on milk from the mother. Echidnas may live as long as 50 years.

A.J.C./J.J.M.

The echidna (above), or spiny anteater, lives in Australia, New Guinea, and Tasmania. If the echidna is threatened, it may roll up in a ball and expose its spines to its enemy, or it may burrow into the ground for protection.

ECHINODERMATA (i kī′ nə dər′ mət ə) Echinodermata is a phylum of marine animals. They are invertebrates. Included in Echinodermata are the starfish, brittlestar, sea urchin, sand dollar, sea lily, and sea cucumber. They are found in every ocean. Echinoderms live near the shore and at the bottom of the deepest parts of the ocean. They are very abundant. Some stay in one place, others float with the water currents, but most slowly crawl along the ocean floor. Many

Echinoderms shown below (left to right) are: star-fish, sea cucumber, brittle star, and feather star.

move by using small suckerlike projections called tube feet. They feed by filter feeding, picking food particles off the sea floor, or preying on other animals.

Members of Echinodermata have bodies which are round or which have arms and legs growing out in a circular manner. Under a thin layer of skin, they have a chalky skeleton. Echinoderms do not have brains. They breath through gills.   S.R.G./R.J.B.

ECHO (ek′ ō) An echo is a sound that has been reflected (bounced back) from a surface. If a person shouts in a large valley, he usually soon hears the echo of his shout. The sound has reflected from rocks in the valley. The sound takes time to get back to the caller because sound travels in air at a fixed speed. Sound waves travel about 1.6 km [1 mi] in five seconds. A person may hear more than one echo from just one sound. The sound waves bounce from place to place and may produce several echoes.

Sometimes an echo is not heard even though the reflected sound waves reach the ear. The echo may not be heard if the original sound is too weak, or if the reflecting object is too small. It is very difficult to tell the difference between the sound and its echo if the reflecting object is less than 9 m [30 ft] away.

Echoes can help a person find out how far he is away from echo-producing objects. It takes 10 seconds for sound to reach an object 1.6 km [1 mi] away and return. Therefore, a person who wants to find out how wide a canyon is may stand at the edge of the canyon and shout. If he hears the echo five seconds later, he can assume that the canyon is about 0.8 km [0.5 mi] in width.

Sound waves traveling through water also produce echoes. Sonar uses underwater echoes to measure depth and to locate underwater objects. It is used to locate underwater channels and can even detect schools of fish. *See also* RADAR; SONAR; SOUND.   J.J.A./J.T.

ECLIPSE (i klips′) An eclipse occurs when a heavenly body is obscured by a shadow or by another heavenly body. There are two kinds of eclipses visible from the earth: a solar eclipse and a lunar eclipse.

A solar eclipse is an eclipse of the sun. It occurs when the moon moves directly into line between the sun and the earth, so that its shadow falls on the earth. If the sun seems to be covered completely, it is called a total eclipse. During a total eclipse, the day seems to turn to night. It lasts for a maximum of 7 minutes 40 seconds. During a total eclipse, the outer atmosphere of the sun, called the

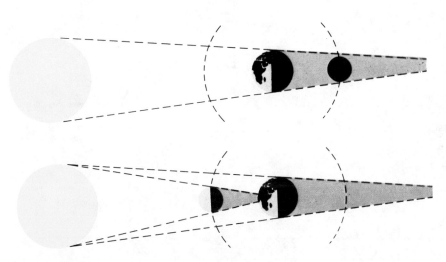

A lunar eclipse (top left) occurs when the earth passes between the moon and sun, casting its shadow over the moon. A solar eclipse (bottom left) occurs when the moon passes between the sun and earth, casting its shadow over part of the earth.

The total solar eclipse of June 30, 1973, seen from a ship off the coast of northwest Africa, is pictured (facing left). A solar eclipse occurs when the moon moves directly into line between the sun and the earth. If the sun seems to be covered completely, it is called a total eclipse.

corona, becomes visible. This aspect of eclipses is of great interest to astronomers.

Not all solar eclipses are total. There is an annular eclipse, where just the middle of the sun is blocked by the moon. In most eclipses, only part of the sun is covered. These are called partial eclipses. Solar eclipses are rare, and only visible from a small area on the earth. Looking directly at a solar eclipse may severely damage the eyes.

A lunar eclipse occurs when the earth is directly between the sun and the moon, so that the moon lies in the shadow of the earth. A lunar eclipse can usually be seen by all people on the night side of the earth. The moon takes on a reddish color during a lunar eclipse because of light being bent by the earth's atmosphere onto the moon.

For thousands of years, eclipses have fascinated as well as confused people. Many people saw solar eclipses as bad omens. Others, like the Babylonians, kept accurate records of eclipses and discovered their regular cycle. *See also* ASTRONOMY. J.M.C./C.R.

ECLIPTIC (i klip′ tik) The ecliptic is the sun's apparent path through the celestial sphere. The plane of the ecliptic is the plane in which the earth travels in orbit around the sun. Since the moon and the planets are roughly in the same plane, they also follow the ecliptic. *See also* ASTRONOMY; CELESTIAL SPHERE.

J.M.C./C.R.

ECOLOGY (i käl′ ə jē) Ecology is the study of organisms and their relationship to other organisms and to their surroundings, or environment. It is a branch of biology. A biologist may study a mouse to find out how big it is, what color it is, and how long it lives. An ecologist would study what plants a mouse eats, what animals eat the mouse, and how the numbers of mice affect the numbers of the animals that eat it. The word ecology is frequently misused. People often speak incorrectly of "protecting the ecology of a lake." They should say "protecting the environment of a lake." The environment is the surroundings of a lake. Ecology is the study of those surroundings.

Ecology examines historical events. Stone Age hunters may have been responsible for the extinction of many species of mammals in North America. Technology can change many things. We can dig new lakes, drain old ones, build dams, and even remove mountains. Sometimes, when we change things, we accidentally change other things we did not intend to change. In the 1960s, the Egyptians built the huge Aswan dam on the Nile River. The purpose of the dam was to provide water for farmers' fields. It did that, but it also did much more. The extra water behind the dam provided a breeding place for a mosquito that carries the disease bilharzia. Bilharzia is now spreading throughout Eygpt. The dam also stopped rich silt from passing downstream to other fields along the river. These fields are now low in nutrients and no longer yield good crops. (*See* AGRICULTURE.) In addition, the fish that used to gather at the mouth of the Nile River in the Mediterranean Sea are now gone. All of these things make life harder for the Egyptians.

Ecologists now try to learn more about the environment so they can predict changes before they can occur. In the early 1970s, the United States was planning on building a number of large jet airplanes called Supersonic Transports (SSTs). Ecologists predicted that the jets would damage the environment in the atmosphere. The SSTs were not built.

Ecologists know that people form one small part of a very complicated system on earth. We depend on many things. Many things depend on us. If we are to live successfully on earth, we must learn to live with the natural environment, and to be careful how we change it. *See also* CONSERVATION; POLLUTION.   S.R.G./R.J.B.

ECOSYSTEM (ē' kō sis' təm) Ecology refers to the relation of organisms with their environment and other organisms. Ecologists have coined the word *ecosystem* from ecological system. An ecosystem is any naturally occurring unit that includes living and nonliving elements which interact to produce a stable system.

An ecosystem can be a very small unit, such as the organisms that inhabit an animal's intestines or those that live on a decaying log. A larger, more complex ecosystem may include all the living and nonliving elements that form a pond or those that form a wooded preserve. The largest ecosystem is called the biosphere, which is the entire portion of earth which holds life. If life is found on other planets, then it would make sense to compare biospheres.

Human beings share the earth with nearly 10 million different species of living things, including plants, animals, insects, and microorganisms. On any area of earth, the populations of plants, animals, and microorganisms make up a biological community. The community is bound together by a complex web of relationships.

Ecologists describe ecosystems by using certain terms. The environment includes such nonliving elements as light, temperature, rain, wind, fire, and soil texture. Chemical processes occur in the environment, including the composition of water in either liquid or gas form, air pollutants, and the composition of soil bearing salt minerals or acids.

Environments may be freshwater, terrestrial, or marine. Some freshwater environments include standing water, such as that found in ponds, lakes, swamps, and bogs. Other freshwater environments consist of running water, such as that found in streams,

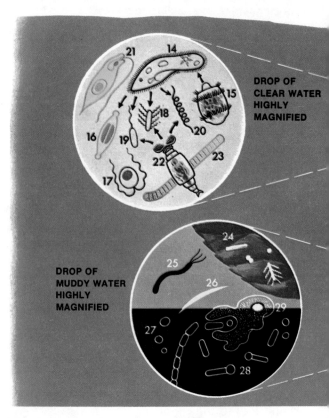

Macroscopic (visible to the human eye) pond life in the illustration above includes; (1) duck feeding on underwater plant; (2) hydra feeding on (3) water flea; (4) frog feeding on fly; (5) arrowhead (an aquatic plant); (6) pond snail; (7) duckweed (the smallest aquatic flower); (8) water scorpion and (9) minnow, both feeding on tadpoles; (10) dragonfly; (11) dragonfly larva feeding on (12) small annelid worm; (13) pond skater. These pond life forms make up an ecosystem.

rivers, and springs.

The terrestrial environment is divided into units called biomes. The various biomes include deserts, tundra (treeless plains), alpine meadows, grasslands, savannas (open grassland with scattered shrubs, bushes, and trees), woodlands, evergreen forests, mixed broadleaf and evergreen forests, and tropical rain forests.

The marine environment consists of all seas and oceans. The living parts of a marine ecosystem may include all algae and plants, shellfish, fishes, sea birds, marine mammals,

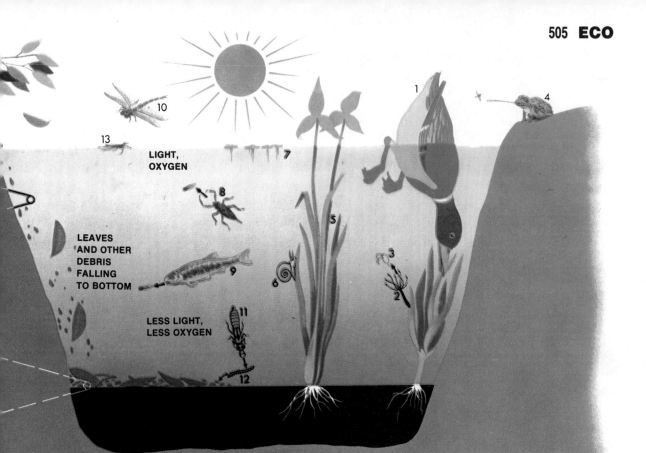

A typical pond contains many animals and plants, some microscopic and others macroscopic. The illustration above shows some of these organisms and some of the ways in which they support each other's lives to form a balanced ecosystem. The pond's microscopic life (left) is shown in two magnified drops of water—one from the light, oxygenated water, one from the dark, oxygenless mud.

Microscopic pond life (far left) includes: (14) paramecium being attacked by (15) didinium; (16) diatom; (17) small flagellate; (18 and 19) aerobic bacteria; (20) spirochete; (21) euglena; (22) rotifer; (23) oscillatoria; (24) bacteria feeding on leaf; (25) spirillum, a large bacterium; (26) another diatom; (27 and 28) anaerobic bacteria; (29) amoeba feeding on bacteria and diatoms.

and microorganisms. The nonliving parts may include ocean water, ice floes, ocean floor, rocky coasts, and climate conditions. For a smaller marine ecosystem, an ecologist may consider only plankton, the tiny plants and animals that drift in the ocean and are at the mercy of the currents.

Communities of living things inhabit an environment. The population of a community consists of groups within a single species or several species that live together casually in the same area. For instance, giraffe, zebra, and several antelope species often share the same range on an African savanna. All popu-

lations that occupy a geographic area are called the biotic community.

The habitat is the particular environment in which a population lives. There are many diverse habitats, and some habitats provide a home for tens of thousands of life forms. Cactus plants are found in dry desert areas; catfish live in slow-moving streams and lakes; pronghorn antelope range across the open western grasslands. Each plant or animal population has a certain niche within its community and its ecosystem. Among animal populations, this niche is determined by plant-eating or predator habits.

In each biotic community, an energy flow takes place. Food energy flows from one form of life to another, forming a food chain. When several food chains are interrelated, the energy flow is complex, and the system is called a food web.

Green plants provide the basic food source of all animal populations. The sun is the source of all energy that runs the ecosystem. On land and in the seas, green plants obtain energy from solar radiation in the form of light. Green plants also obtain energy from minerals and nutrients in the soil. In any food chain, green plants are the most efficient producers of food and energy.

Herbivores, or plant-eating animals, are called primary consumers because they eat the green plants. Carnivores, or flesh-eating animals, are called secondary consumers. Deer, rabbits, and mice eat grass, seeds, leaves, and crops, obtaining energy and nutrients directly from plant foods. Bobcats, wolves, and foxes are carnivores. They obtain energy and nutrients by eating the animals that ate the green plants. Plant and animal remains deteriorate because of decomposers such as beetles, earthworms, mushrooms, and various microorganisms. As energy flows through a food chain, it is recycled over and over again and declines.

In understanding the complex interrelationships in an ecosystem, ecologists also study animal habits and behavior patterns, social adaptations, territories, and nesting and feeding sites. If something disrupts the natural order of the system, the entire ecology may be threatened. Plants may not grow well and may not reseed; animals may not breed and reproduce.

Studying ecosystems and resolving conflicts between the different uses of ecosystems can help improve the quality of life and conserve natural environments for future generations. *See also* CONSERVATION; ECOLOGY; ENVIRONMENT; POLLUTION.

D.A.T./G.D.B.

Cactus plants (below) have adapted to the dry habitat of the desert ecosystem.

In contrast with the dry desert ecosystem is the rainforest (above).

ECZEMA (eg′ zə mə) Eczema is a common form of dermatitis, which is a rash or inflammation of the skin. The skin turns red. Fluid-filled pimples, called vesicles, may form. Also, crusts and scales may develop on the surface of the skin. Eczema usually causes the skin to itch. If scratched, the skin may become infected by bacteria.

Doctors believe eczema is caused by an allergy. The allergy results from an extreme reaction to some substances. The substances may be in something the person eats or touches.

Some plants give off certain substances that cause eczema. For instance, oils produced by poison ivy cause a form of eczema when the oils come in contact with a person's skin.

Curing a person with eczema is often very difficult. The most important part in treating eczema is to find out what caused the rash. Doctors test how people react to various substances. This helps doctors find the cause of eczema. Treatment usually involves removing the cause.   J.J.A./J.J.F.

EDISON, THOMAS ALVA (1847–1931) Thomas Alva Edison (ed′ i sən) was one of the greatest inventors in history. He changed the lives of millions of people with inventions such as the electric light, phonograph, and motion picture camera. His concept of inexpensive electricity generated by huge electric power stations made it possible for people to enjoy the benefits of electricity in their homes. Edison patented 1,093 inventions in his lifetime.

He improved the inventions of other people, like the telephone, typewriter, and electric generator. He came close to inventing the radio. Edison predicted the use of atomic energy, and experimented in the field of medicine. He always tried to develop practical devices that would need little maintenance or repair. Edison loved to experiment and was never discouraged by failure. Once, when about 10,000 experiments with a storage battery failed to produce results, a friend tried to console him. "Why, I have not failed," he said. "I've just found 10,000 ways that won't work."

Edison had only three months of formal schooling. He was born in Ohio, but spent most of his life in Menlo Park, New Jersey, a suburb of the city of Newark. He became known as the "Wizard of Menlo Park" because of his many inventions.

In 1869, Edison made improvements in the stock ticker, an electric device that transmits news of stock prices and displays them on a paper tape. He patented his improvements, and was paid $40,000 for them by the leading manufacturer of stock tickers. That was a large amount of money in 1869. Edison used it to open a workshop and laboratory in Menlo Park.

Edison improved the typewriter in 1874 by substituting metal parts for wood parts. In 1876, he improved the telephone by adding a carbon transmitter. Edison astounded the world in 1877 with his invention of the phonograph, or "talking machine," as it was then called.

In 1879, the inventor worked out the principles for electric lighting. He experimented for two more years to find a filament, or wire, that would give good light when electricity flowed through it. On October 19, 1879, Edison placed a filament of carbonized thread in a bulb. When electricity flowed through the thread it glowed brilliantly, producing a bright light. A short time later, Edison designed one of the world's first electric power generating stations.

Edison developed a motion picture camera in the late 1880s. He experimented with it in a small building near his workshop. The building was called "The Black Mariah" because it was painted black inside and out. Edison made many experimental films inside the "The Black Mariah," including the first boxing match ever filmed. In 1914, he combined the motion picture camera with the phonograph to produce the first "talking pictures." Until then, motion pictures had been silent. The actors' words had been shown on the screen in printed form. Edison's "talking pictures" revolutionized the motion picture industry.

In later years, Edison invented, or improved on, the storage battery, cement mixer, dictaphone, and a duplicating machine. His last patented invention was a method for making artificial rubber from goldenrod plants.

Throughout Edison's life, his work was his greatest joy and companion. He spent long hours every day in his workshop. The inventor received many awards for his achievements. The United States presented him with the Distinguished Service Medal for his de-

sign work on torpedoes in World War I. France awarded him the Legion of Honor. President Dwight D. Eisenhower declared his Menlo Park workshop a national monument in 1956. Henry Ford, the well-known industrialist, once suggested that the period when Edison lived should be called the Age of Edison because of the great inventor's many contributions to mankind.

W.R.P./D.G.F.

EEL (ēl) An eel is a long, snakelike fish that lives in both salt water and fresh water. It is a member of the order Anguilliformes. There are eight families and 55 species of eels in North America. All but the American eel live just in the ocean. Many of these saltwater eels, such as the moray eel, grow large and have many sharp teeth. They can be dangerous to skin divers. The electric eel of South America resembles the true eels in shape. It can produce electricity that can kill or stun other animals. (*See* ELECTRIC FISH.)

The American eel is a member of the family Anguillidae. Adults live in freshwater streams and ponds. When it is time for them to reproduce, they swim down the rivers and travel to the Sargasso Sea, an area in the Atlantic Ocean southwest of Bermuda, where they spawn. (*See* SPAWNING.) The young eels (called elvers) swim to reach the stream in which their parents lived. Males, which grow to 0.6 m [2 ft] in length, do not travel many kilometers up river, but the females, which grow to 1.21 m [4 ft] in length, may ascend the river thousands of kilometers. They even find their way into land-locked ponds and lakes. Eels can travel through underground water passages. This eel migration that goes from fresh water to salt water to spawn is called catadromy. The American eel is the only catadromous fish in North America. Many fishes are anadromous, traveling from salt water to fresh water to spawn. (*See* MIGRATION; SALMON.)

S.R.G./E.C.M.

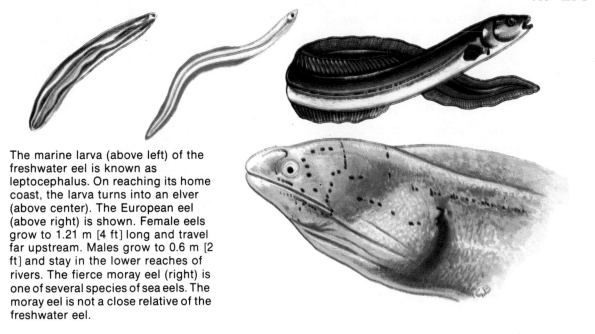

The marine larva (above left) of the freshwater eel is known as leptocephalus. On reaching its home coast, the larva turns into an elver (above center). The European eel (above right) is shown. Female eels grow to 1.21 m [4 ft] long and travel far upstream. Males grow to 0.6 m [2 ft] and stay in the lower reaches of rivers. The fierce moray eel (right) is one of several species of sea eels. The moray eel is not a close relative of the freshwater eel.

EFFERVESCENCE (ef′ ər ves′ əns) Effervescence is the making of small bubbles of gas in a liquid. The gas may be made by a chemical reaction in the liquid.

Effervescence can be seen when adding water to tablets or powders that are meant to calm upset stomachs. The ingredients include weak acids and bicarbonates. They dissolve in the water and react together, producing bubbles of carbon dioxide gas.

Effervescence also occurs when a gas under pressure dissolves in a liquid, and the pressure is then released. This happens, for example, when the cap is removed from a bottle of soda. Carbon dioxide gas dissolved in the soda water leaves the solution and forms bubbles.   J.J.A./A.D.

EFFICIENCY (i fish′ ən sē) In physics, efficiency is the amount of energy a machine provides compared to the amount of energy a machine uses. In other words, efficiency is the amount of work we get out of a machine divided by the amount of energy put into the machine. This can be written as a formula or equation.

$$\text{Efficiency} = \frac{\text{output energy or work}}{\text{input energy or work}}$$

Much of the energy put into a machine is lost as heat in overcoming friction. So the efficiency is always less than one. Scientists express efficiency in percentages. For example, the efficiency rating of a four stroke cycle gasoline engine may be as low as 25%. The inefficiency of the engine is due to the high heat loss in the cooling system and the friction in its moving parts.

In all machines, the input energy is never fully converted to output energy. For example, an electric motor may consume 500 watts of electricity to provide 400 watts of useful mechanical power. Power is the rate at which work is done.

$$\text{Efficiency} = \frac{\text{output work}}{\text{input energy}}$$

$$= \frac{400}{500} = 0.8 = 80\%$$

The 100 watts of input power which are not converted to useful output power are converted to heat in the motor. Heat is produced by the electric current passing through the coils or wires in the motor. Heat is also produced by mechanical friction of the motor's moving parts.

The term efficiency is also used in connection with other things besides machines. An electrical transformer can be more than 98% efficient. The human body has an efficiency of about 24%. *See also* ENERGY; MACHINE.

J.J.A./J.T.

EFFLORESCENCE (ef lə res' əns) Efflorescence is a change that occurs in certain crystals. They become white and powdery when the air is dry. The change occurs because molecules of water evaporate from the crystals. Washing soda is an example of a substance that effloresces. It contains ten molecules of water for each molecule of sodium carbonate. Its formula can be written $Na_2CO_3 \cdot 10\ H_2O$. The water in the crystals is called water of crystallization. Up to nine molecules of this water can be lost from each washing soda molecule. This means that the crystals become covered with dry powder when the air is dry. The opposite of efflorescence is called deliquescence. When this happens, crystals take up water from the air around them. D.M.H.W./A.D.

EGGPLANT (eg' plant') The eggplant *(Solanum melongena)* is a perennial plant. It produces a large, edible, egg-shaped fruit also called eggplant. The eggplant is a member of the nightshade family and is closely related to the potato. It is native to India and is now grown throughout the world in warm or tropical areas.

The plant is bushlike, growing as tall as 2 m [6.6 ft]. It has large, grayish, prickly leaves, and purple or blue flowers measuring about 5 cm [2 in] in diameter. The fruit reaches a length of 5 to 30 cm [2 to 12 in] and may be purple, brown, yellow, red, white, or striped. The purple variety is the most popular for eating, but it provides few calories or vitamins. A.J.C./F.W.S.

The eggplant (above) is most familiar as a purple fruit. The purple variety is most popular for eating. However, eggplant may be brown, red, yellow, white, or striped. The eggplant is native to India.

EGRET (ē' grət) The egret is any of several species of long-legged birds belonging to the heron family and characterized by long, elegant feathers called plumes. Egrets usually live in warm areas in or near lakes or marshes, though some species inhabit open grasslands. The egret has a "S" shaped neck, and keeps its head tucked between its shoulders when in flight. The plumes appear only during mating season. They were at one time considered valuable additions to hats and Oriental ceremonial dress. Egrets were once in danger of extinction. Hunters killed millions of them for their plumes and left the helpless young to starve. The Audubon Society and other conservation groups helped establish laws to protect the birds in many areas. (*See* AUDUBON, JOHN JAMES.) There are now protective sanctuaries in South Carolina, Florida, Louisiana, Texas, and in some other states.

The most common egrets in the United States are the great white egret (once called the American egret) and the cattle egret. The great white egret (*Egretta alba*) is about 90 cm [35 in] tall with a wingspan of about 1.8 m [6 ft]. This species produces the longest plumes. The smaller cattle egret (*Ardeola ibis*) stands about 50 cm [20 in] tall with a wingspan of about 1 m [3 ft]. The cattle egret feeds on small insects stirred up by the movement of cattle through open grasslands. Some cattle egrets ride on the backs of the cattle and water buffalo. They pick ticks and other insects from the animal's skin. (*See* SYMBIOSIS.) Cattle egrets came to South America from Africa about 50 years ago and only reached the United States after World War II (1945).   A.J.C./L.L.S.

EHRLICH, PAUL (1854–1915) Paul Ehrlich (ār' lik), a German bacteriologist, became known for discovering the drug arsphenamine, also called Salvarsan. Salvarsan was the first effective treatment for syphilis. Ehrlich believed that, since certain dyes stick to certain living tissues and stain them, it ought to be possible to find a poisonous dye that could stick to germs and kill them. In 1910, after many tests, Salvarsan was found suitable for this purpose. Salvarsan is also called "606" because it was the 606th compound tested.

Ehrlich also did much work on the use of dyes for studying living tissues, and on the bacteria that cause tuberculosis. He also worked on increasing immunity to disease. He developed a diphtheria antitoxin. In 1908, for his work on immunity, Ehrlich shared the Nobel Prize for Medicine with Elie Metchnikoff.   J.J.A./D.G.F.

EIDER (īd' ər) The eider is a sea duck that belongs to the family Anatidae. It is a heavy-bodied duck with a short neck and wings. There are four species of eiders in North America. Two species are found mainly in Alaska. The other two species live throughout the northern part of the continent. The feathers from these ducks were once commonly used as stuffing for pillows, mattresses, sleeping bags, and clothing. They are very light but hold warmth well. *See also* DUCK.   S.R.G./L.L.S.

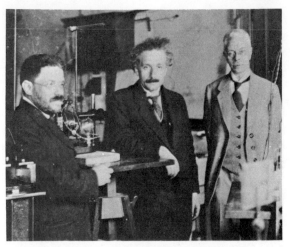

Albert Einstein, one of the great pioneers of modern physics, is pictured in the center.

EINSTEIN, ALBERT (1879–1955) Albert Einstein (īn' shtīn), a German-American scientist, was one of the greatest contributors to modern physics. Einstein was born in Ulm, Germany, but soon moved to Munich. After public school in Munich and in Aarau, Switzerland, Einstein studied math and physics at the Swiss Polytechnic Institute in Zurich. He was graduated in 1900. He became a Swiss citizen at the age of 22. From 1902 to 1909, he was employed at the patent office in Berne, Switzerland. During these years, Einstein published the first part of his famous theory of relativity. In 1914, he became a professor at the Prussian Academy of Science in Berlin, Germany. In 1921, Einstein received the Nobel Prize for physics. In 1932, Princeton University offered Einstein a lifetime professorship. He accepted the offer, providing he could divide his time between Princeton and the Prussian Academy of Sciences. Conditions in Germany in 1933 made it very difficult for Jewish people to live there. In 1940, Einstein became a United States citizen.

Einstein's ideas Einstein's theory of relativity greatly changed scientific thought with new concepts of time, space, motion, and gravitation. His formula, $E = mc^2$ is one of the most important equations in science. In this formula, *E* stands for energy, *m* for mass, and c^2 for the speed of light multiplied by itself. This formula shows that matter, which is any material or substance, if completely changed to energy such as heat or light, would produce a huge amount of energy.

With the knowledge of this formula, it became possible to imagine the atomic bomb and later to make it.

Many of Einstein's ideas were difficult to understand. Some of them, however, came out of other quite basic ideas. For example, to a person living in New York, Pittsburgh is west. To a person living in Arizona, Pittsburgh is east. The direction of Pittsburgh is relative. It depends on where a person is. The same kind of idea is true for things that move. For example, if a person is sitting in a train, and another train begins to pass by the window, it is puzzling for the person to tell which train is moving. Therefore, motion is relative. Einstein built on these ideas. He included the motion of light itself in his thinking. He joined together space and time in a new theory of relativity. (*See* RELATIVITY.)

Einstein also made great advances in the quantum theory. He suggested that light could be thought of as a stream of tiny particles called quanta. Using his theory of quanta, Einstein explained the photoelectric effect. He showed that when quanta of light energy strike atoms in certain metals, the quanta force the atoms in the metal to release electrons.

Einstein also studied the Brownian movement, an irregular motion of tiny particles suspended in a liquid or gas. This movement showed that atoms and molecules are always in motion.

Einstein was also concerned with the force of gravity and electromagnetism. Einstein believed that gravitation is not caused by some mysterious force in matter. He thought that gravitation is caused by inertia itself. Inertia means that a body cannot by itself change its state of rest or motion. Unless some outside force affects an object, the object con-tinues to rest or move as it was moving. Einstein also thought that the inertia of a body forces it to take a certain path through a space, which would bend when it came near a large mass of matter, such as the sun.

Einstein tried to combine electromagnetism and gravitational force in a single theory called unified field theory. Einstein failed to establish such a theory. He spent the last 25 years of his life working on it.

J.J.A./D.G.F.

EINSTEINIUM (īn stī′ nē əm) Einsteinium is a radioactive element. The chemical symbol for einsteinium is Es, and its atomic number is 99. It has an isotope, Es-254, with a half-line of 270 days. It is named for the great physicist Albert Einstein. It does not occur naturally. It was first detected after a hydrogen bomb explosion in 1952, having been formed during the explosion. It is produced by nuclear bombardment of certain heavy elements.

D.W./J.R.W.

The eland, found in southeast Africa, is the tallest and heaviest of the antelopes.

ELAND (ē′ lənd) The eland is the largest of the antelopes, standing 1.8 m [6 ft] tall at the shoulder and weighing as much as 950 kg [2090 lb]. It has spirally twisted horns, about 1 m [3.3 ft] long, humped shoulders, and a dewlap (flap of skin) hanging from the neck.

The eland usually has 8 to 15 vertical stripes on its sides and a black stripe along its back. This mammal is native to Africa and grazes in herds of 200 or more in open plains and light forests. The eland is a valuable farm animal. It is easily trained, has an immunity to many local diseases, and can go for weeks without water.

There are two major species of elands. The common eland (*Taurotragus oryx*) is pale brown in color and lives in southern Africa. The larger Derby eland (*Taurotragus derbianus*) is reddish brown, has heavier horns, and lives in central Africa.   A.J.C./J.J.M.

ELASTICITY (i las′ tis′ ət ē) If an object is stretched and let go, two things can happen. It can stay stretched or it can return to its original shape. If it springs back, it is said to have elasticity. Rubber and steel are both elastic materials.

An object is stretched by applying a force. For an elastic object, the amount it stretches is proportional to the force. For example, if the force is doubled the object is stretched through twice the distance. This is called Hooke's law. It was first discovered by Robert Hooke, an English physicist.

An elastic body can only be stretched a certain distance. If more force is applied to it, two things can happen. It can break or it can stay stretched at the same distance. When this happens it has passed its elastic limit. If it is stretched still more, the yield point is reached. Then only a small extra force stretches it a lot. Narrow necks start to appear. Eventually one of the necks gets so narrow that it breaks.

When an object is stretched, it is said to be under stress. There are other ways of stressing an object. One way is by twisting it. This is called torsion. Only elastic materials return to their original shape when twisted and then let go. Non-elastic materials stay twisted. Hooke's law also applies to this type of stress. In this case, you measure the angle that the object is twisted through. For an elastic object, this angle is proportional to the twisting force. Again there is an elastic limit. If the object is twisted too far, it will remain twisted.

There are other important types of stress. One is called the shear stress. This stress is like pushing along the top of a deck of cards. When you do this, the deck deforms and the cards spread out. With a shear stress, objects deform and spread in the same way. Another kind of stress is when you squash an object on all sides. This happens to objects at the bottom of the sea. Hooke's law applies to both these stresses.

A golf ball (above) goes out of shape when hit by a club. Because the ball is made of very elastic materials, it resumes its original spherical shape as soon as it leaves the club.

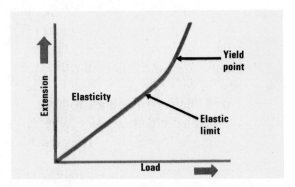

A graph (above) plots the extension of a body against the force acting on it, and a straight line occurs. The body loses elasticity past its elastic limit and stretches past the yield point.

All solids are made up of atoms. The atoms are held together by bonds. The bonds are like springs. When an object is stressed, the atoms are pulled apart. This means that the bonds are stretched. When the stress is released, the atoms spring back. All solids have weak points, such as a crack on the surface. The bonds at these points break more easily than others. When an object is stretched, these are the first bonds to break. This happens to brittle objects such as porcelain.

Rubber is a very elastic material. It stretches very easily. It does this because of its atoms. They are arranged in long molecules. (*See* MOLECULE.) These molecules are coiled. When rubber is stretched, the molecules uncoil. Only a small force is needed to uncoil the molecules. M.E./J.T.

ELASTIN (i las′ tən) Elastin is a protein found in the elastic fibers and elastic tissues of an animal's body. It is made of a large molecule which can coil or uncoil to give elastin its elastic properties. (*See* ELASTICITY.) Elastin makes up the yellow, branching elastic fibers found in connective tissue. Elastin is also part of the elastic tissues in the fat of an animal's body. A.J.C./E.R.L.

ELDERBERRY (el′ dər ber′ ē) The elderberry is a small black or red berry produced by the elder plant. The elder plant is any of 40 species of trees or shrubs belonging to the honeysuckle family and growing in temperate regions throughout the world. The elder plant grows as tall as 75 cm [30 in] and has leaves divided into five pointed and toothed leaflets. There are large clusters of small, white, saucer-shaped flowers which are followed by small fruits called elderberries. Elderberries are a food source for wildlife. They can also be processed into medicines or wine. A.J.C./M.H.S.

ELECTRIC BELL (i lek′ trik bel′) The doorbell in the average home is an electric bell that works on a principle of electromagnetism. A piece of iron can be made magnetic when an electric current is passed through a coil of wire wrapped around it. The iron and the coil form an electromagnet.

In the electric bell, a piece of iron, called an armature, is drawn toward the ends of a U-shaped piece of iron when the U-shaped piece is magnetized. The electric current also passes through the armature to a contact. When the bell is not being rung, the armature is held against this contact by a spring. The pressing of a button starts the current flowing from a battery. The armature is pulled away from the contact. At the same time, a hammer attached to the armature strikes a bell. However, separating the armature from the contact stops the electric current, and therefore the magnetism of the U-shaped piece of iron. The armature is then drawn back to the contact by the spring. This order of events is repeated as long as the button remains pressed producing the rapid ringing sound of the bell. J.J.A./J.T.

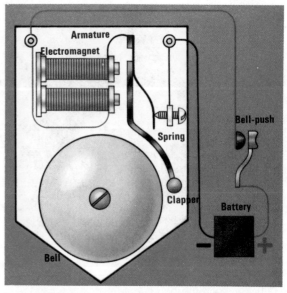

The diagram (above) shows a battery-powered house door-bell, a common type of electric bell.

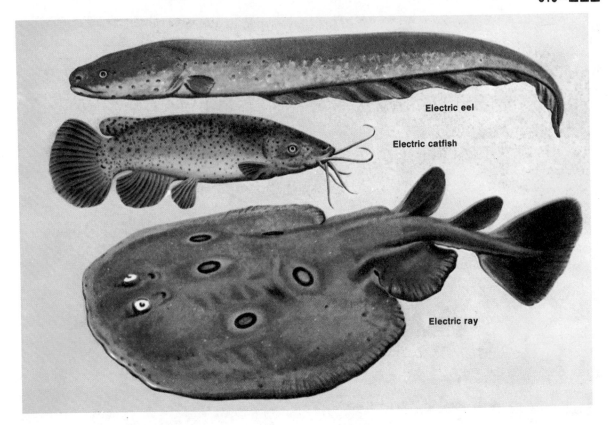

Electric eel

Electric catfish

Electric ray

The best-known electric fish are the electric eel (which produces shocks of up to 550 volts), the electric catfish, and the electric ray.

ELECTRIC FISH (i lek′ trik fish) A number of species of fishes are able to produce electricity in their bodies. The better-known electric fishes are the electric eel, the electric catfish, and the electric ray. (*See* CAT-FISH; EEL; RAY.) They produce electricity with special muscles. Most muscles contract when a nerve stimulates them. A special "electric" muscle cannot contract. When a nerve stimulates it, an electrical shock is produced. The electric eel is able to produce a discharge up to 550 volts. This is enough to stun a large animal that is standing in the water.

Electric fishes usually use the electricity to defend themselves. Some of the fishes use it to stun and capture prey. The electrical field is also used by fish to find their way in muddy water, similar to the way radar is used.

S.R.G./E.C.M.

ELECTRICITY

Electricity (i lek′ tris′ ət ē) is a property of nature that we usually know as electric current. We cannot see it, but we can see its effects. Rubbing two things together sometimes produces electricity. This happens when you take off a nylon sweater. The nylon rubs against your hair or your clothing. The electricity causes crackling and sparks. This effect has been known for thousands of years. A Greek philosopher called Thales noticed it in 600 B.C. He rubbed a piece of amber. When he did this, the amber tried to pull things towards it. This is because it had an electric charge. This is how electricity got its name. It comes from the Greek for amber, *elektron*.

Another effect of electricity is lightning. This was not always known. The American scientist Benjamin Franklin first showed this

connection between electricity and lightning.

In 1780, another effect of electricity was noticed. An Italian named Luigi Galvani touched the back leg of a dead frog with his knife. When he did this, the leg twitched. He guessed that this was due to electricity. Another Italian, Count Alessandro Volta, found out what was happening. The knife was made out of brass and iron. These metals acted on a certain liquid in the frog's leg. This produced electricity and led to the discovery of the voltaic cell and the battery. (*See* BATTERY.) They were both invented in 1800.

Soon afterward, scientists started to study electrochemistry. In the 1830s, the English scientist Michael Faraday discovered the laws of electrolysis. By this time electric circuits were being built. In a circuit, an electric field is established in a wire, and it is possible that a current travels along a wire. In 1831, Faraday made a great discovery. He took a circuit that did not have any current running through it. Then he moved it around inside a magnetic field. This produced a current in the circuit. Faraday had discovered a very good way of producing electricity. This method is still used today in generators. Generators produce electricity for homes and factories. Faraday also discovered the opposite effect. He placed a wire with a current running through it between the poles of a magnet. When the current changed, the wire moved. This effect is now used in electric motors. The links between electricity and magnetism are studied in electromagnetism.

Soon large generators were being built. Electricity was beginning to come into use in the United States and Europe. Industry began to use electric motors to replace some steam engines.

New inventions   Many new inventions were made. An American inventor named Thomas

Electricity in nature is typified by lightning—the flashing of light produced by a release of atmospheric electricity from a cloud.

The electric light bulb typifies the harnessing of electricity. The first light bulb was made by Thomas Edison in 1879.

The tower of the wind turbine (facing left) is 60 m [200 ft] high, and the blades are 91 m [300 ft] from tip to tip. The turbine can generate 2.5 megawatts of electricity.

Edison made an important discovery. When a current passes through a wire, the wire is heated. Edison found a way of making the wire become so hot that it glowed. This effect is now used in the electric light and the electric heater which provide light and heat in millions of homes throughout the world.

In 1837, the telegraph was invented by two English scientists, Sir Charles Wheatstone and W. F. Cooke. Samuel F. B. Morse also worked on the telegraph in the United States. Morse invented the relay. This device allowed telegraph messages to be sent over long distances. In 1851, the first telegraph cable under the sea was laid. It linked Britain and France. In 1866, a cable was laid under the Atlantic Ocean. It linked the United States and Britain. Then, in 1875, Alexander Graham Bell invented the telephone.

Another discovery concerned with electricity was that of radio waves. In 1873, James Clerk Maxwell proved with mathematics that radio waves should exist. In 1887, they were generated electrically by Heinrich Hertz. The first person to think of using them for communicating was Guglielmo Marconi. He sent his first radio message across the Atlantic Ocean in 1901.

Radio broadcasting did not start until after World War I. Before broadcasting could start, amplifiers had to be invented. In 1907, Lee de Forest invented the triode vacuum tube. This tube can be used for amplifying. A few years later, engineers realized this and soon broadcasting began.

Another very important invention was the cathode-ray tube. These tubes are used in television sets. Before television could be invented, there were many complicated problems to be solved. It was finally invented in 1926 by John Logie Baird in Britain.

During World War II, electronics made great advances. New inventions meant that radar could be used. Radar also uses cathode-ray tubes. Since then, many new electrical machines have been built. Electricity is used in washing machines, dishwashers, trains, and many other kinds of machines.

What is electricity? When scientists discovered electricity, they thought it was a fluid like water. They thought there were two kinds of electricity, one positive and one negative. They thought that electricity was made up of two fluids. That is why they used the term electric current. They also talked about resistance. A high resistance slows down the flow of the fluid. We still use these words today, though we no longer think of electricity as a fluid. Around the 1830s, scientists began to think that electricity might consist of particles. This idea became more and more popular. It was not until 1897 that these particles were discovered by Sir J. J. Thomson. They were called electrons. The electron is a very small particle with a very small electric charge. A typical flashlight bulb uses a current of one ampere. A circuit of one ampere has six billion billion electrons flowing around it every second.

There are several different quantities in electricity. Many different instruments are needed for measuring them. These quantities are measured in different units which are often named for famous scientists. The amount of electric charge is measured in coulombs. This is named for the French physicist, Charles Coulomb. Current is measured in amperes. André Ampère was a French scientist who studied electricity around 1800. The resistance of a material is measured in ohms, after Georg Ohm. (*See* OHM'S LAW.) Potential and electromotive force are measured in volts, after the Italian scientist, Alessandro Volta.   M.E./A.I.

ELECTRICITY SUPPLY (i lek′ tris′ ət ē sə plī′) Electricity is the most important form of power that we have. We use it for heating and lighting in the home. We use electricity for cooking. We use it for TV and radio. We use it in industry to drive hundreds of different

A man (above) is performing maintenance work on a huge electricity generator in a power station. Steam produced by coal, oil, or nuclear energy drives the turbines which power these generators. There are several different kinds of electricity generating stations.

kinds of machinery. It has been estimated that a worker in industry has the equivalent of over 500 slaves working for him because of the electric power that he can use. It is very hard to imagine a world without electricity. For everybody in the country to receive a supply of electricity, huge generating stations are needed. There must also be a network of power supply lines. The power lines that cover the country are called the electricity grid.

Generating stations Most electricity is produced by generating stations that supply

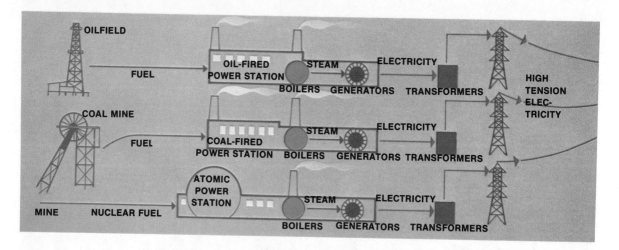

OILFIELD

FUEL

OIL-FIRED POWER STATION · STEAM · ELECTRICITY

BOILERS · GENERATORS · TRANSFORMERS

HIGH TENSION ELEC-TRICITY

COAL MINE

FUEL

COAL-FIRED POWER STATION · STEAM · ELECTRICITY

BOILERS · GENERATORS TRANSFORMERS

MINE · NUCLEAR FUEL

ATOMIC POWER STATION · STEAM · ELECTRICITY

BOILERS · GENERATORS · TRANSFORMERS

The diagram (above) shows in schematized form how electricity is distributed from power stations to industrial users and ordinary homes. Before the electricity goes into individual homes, transformers at local power stations turn the high voltage electricity into low voltage electricity.

Huge transformers (above) in power stations increase the voltage of electricity.

power to wide areas of the country. Some big industries have their own generating stations. This means that they do not have to rely on the public supply. The first electric supply stations were set up in 1882. They were designed by Thomas Edison. He built one in London, England, and two in the United States. These stations supplied direct current to only a few dozen users. In 1886, George Westinghouse built supply stations that produced alternating electric current. Alternating electric current (AC) is safer and more convenient than direct current (DC).

Electricity generating stations are of several different kinds. Some use the energy that comes from water stored behind dams. These are hydroelectric stations. Some generating stations burn oil or coal to heat water and make steam. The steam is then used to turn big turbines. The turbines generate the electricity. Modern generating stations are also designed to use atomic fuel. These are the nuclear or atomic stations.

When the electricity has been produced, it must be distributed. To distribute the electricity, transformers are first used. A transformer increases the voltage of the electricity. The cables that carry electricity in the grid carry it at very high voltage. The voltage of electricity produced by a generator is only a few thousand volts. With the help of a transformer, this becomes many thousands of

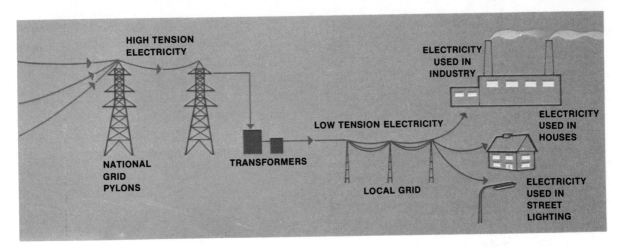

volts. Sometimes hundreds of thousands of volts are used in the power lines. Such a large voltage is used because less power is lost in the cables.

Power lines About half a million miles of power lines are used to supply electricity across the United States. This is long enough to stretch to the moon and back again. The power lines are high-voltage lines. Most users of electricity do not need it at very high voltage. The electricity used by most people is only at about 120 or 200 volts. To turn the high voltage electricity into low voltage, transformers are again used. The transformers are in local power stations. From the local power stations, the electricity is distributed to houses and factories nearby, and to the streets for lighting.

Electricity power lines are made of copper or aluminum. They are insulated. The insulation must be very strong. It is usually plastic or oiled paper, in many layers. In the open country, the supply lines are hung from tall pylons, or towerlike structures. The lines of pylons stretch for miles. In the city, it is often too dangerous to have electric cables hanging overhead. Instead the cables are buried in the ground. Laying cables underground is very expensive. They cost more than building pylon lines and overhead cables. *See also* GENERATOR, ELECTRICAL.   D.W./A.I.

ELECTRIC LIGHT (i lek′ trik līt′) Electricity can be used to produce light in three ways. It can be passed through a wire so that the wire glows red hot or white hot. Electricity can be made to pass through a gas. This makes the gas glow and give off light. It can be passed through special substances that glow when an electric voltage is applied to them.

Light has been produced by passing electricity through wires for over a hundred years. In 1859, Moses Farmer lit his house in Salem, Massachusetts with electric lamps he had invented. The wires in the lamps were made of platinum. The wire that glows in a lamp is called a filament. The inventor Thomas Edison found that better light was produced if the filament were made of carbon. However, such lamps were more difficult to make. They had to have most of the air inside them taken away. Unless the air were removed, the carbon burned when it became hot enough to glow.

Today, the filaments of lamps are often made of the metal tungsten. Tungsten gives a much whiter light than carbon when it glows. The filament is made in a coil shape. The bulb contains the gases nitrogen and argon. These do not react with the metal of the filament. The metal does not burn or evaporate. Most light bulbs in the home use between 40 and 150 watts of electric power. In TV studios and

In the office (above) the entire ceiling has subdued electric lighting, which avoids glare and gives an effect as much like daylight as possible.

in searchlights, there are large tungsten lights that use as much as 30,000 watts.

Many of the lights that are used for street lighting and for business signs are tubes containing gas. When electricity is passed through the gas, the energy makes the atoms of gas glow brightly. Different gases and vapors glow in different colors. Neon glows bright red. Sodium vapor glows yellow. Mercury vapor gives a bluish white light. These lamps are called discharge lamps.

Arc lamps give very bright light. Electricity is made to jump from one electrode to another through the air. In a carbon arc light, the electrodes are rods of carbon. Carbon arc lights are sometimes used for motion picture projectors. They also make very good searchlights.

Another kind of lamp that contains a gas is called a fluorescent lamp. (*See* FLUORESCENCE.) A fluorescent lamp contains mercury vapor. When an electric current is passed through mercury vapor, it produces bluish white light. It also produces invisible rays. These are called ultraviolet rays. The lamp has a special layer of powder inside its glass. The powder is called a phosphor. When a phosphor is struck by ultraviolet rays, it glows. The light it gives off may be white or any of several different colors. Zinc silicate is a phosphor that gives off green light. Calcium

tungstate gives off blue light. Magnesium tungstate produces yellowish white light.

Flat panels of glass can also be used as sources of light. Instead of sticking the phosphor inside the fluorescent tube, it is stuck to the glass like a sandwich between two electrodes. Zinc sulphide is a phosphor that glows when an electric current flows through it.

D.W./J.T.

This French train is powered by electricity.

ELECTRIC MOTOR (i lek′ trik mōt′ ər) An electric motor is a kind of machine. It is a machine that uses the energy of electricity to do work. Electric motors mostly use electrical energy to make wheels turn. A motor that makes wheels and shafts turn is called a rotary machine. There are very many ways in which wheels and shafts turning around can be made to do work for us. Washing machines, vacuum cleaners, drills, and fans all rely on turning parts to do their job. Electric pumps have blades that spin at high speed to push liquids or gases along tubes.

Electric railroad trains and electric automobiles have shafts, gears, and driving wheels that are turned by electric motors. Not all electric motors turn wheels, however. There are modern electric motors that can move loads along tracks without wheels. The tracks must be specially built. Motors like this are called linear induction motors.

Electric motors depend upon electromag-

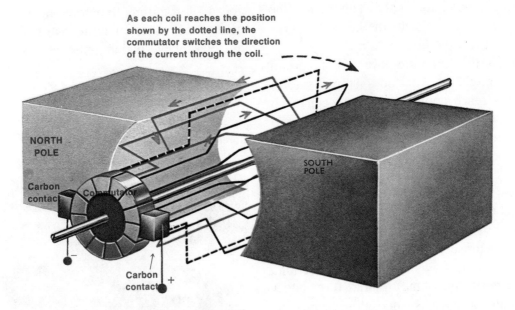

As each coil reaches the position shown by the dotted line, the commutator switches the direction of the current through the coil.

NORTH POLE

SOUTH POLE

Carbon contact

Commutator

Carbon contact

A diagram of a many-coiled DC (direct current) electric motor is shown above. The coils form the armature, which is pivoted on a drive shaft between the north (N) and south (S) poles of a fixed magnet. When current passes through the armature (as shown by arrows) each coil becomes magnetized, and rotates until its N pole is next to the S pole of the fixed magnet. At this point, the commutator switches the direction of the current. The N pole of the coil becomes a S pole and is repelled by the S pole of the fixed magnet, so that rotation continues. A one-coil motor does not run smoothly, because the magnetic force that rotates it varies with the relative positions of the coil and magnet. It also jerks when the commutator switches the current.

netism. Whenever an electric current flows in a wire, the wire acts like a magnet. If the wire is bent into a loop, one side of the loop acts like a north pole and the other side like a south pole. If the wire is bent into many loops, this forms a coil. The coil becomes strongly magnetic. Now it moves just like one magnet does when it comes near to another. The north pole of a magnet is attracted by the south pole of another magnet. It is pushed away, or repelled, by another north pole.

An electric motor has two main parts. One part is fixed. This part is called the stator. Inside the stator is a part that can turn. This is called the rotor, or armature. The rotor consists of coils of wire. They are wound around pieces of soft iron, called cores. The iron increases the strength of the magnetism when electricity passes through the coils. The stator in simple motors is a permanent magnet. (*See* MAGNETISM.) In other motors it is made of

coils of wire, like the rotor. Coils like this are called a field winding.

There are two main kinds of electric motor. One kind uses direct current electricity, or DC. The other uses alternating current, or AC. In a DC motor, the coils of the armature are fed with electric current through pieces of carbon on each side. The pieces of carbon are called brushes. The brushes touch a ring of metal pieces fixed around the shaft of the armature. This ring is called the commutator. Electric current flows from one carbon brush, through the commutator, into the coils of the armature. From the armature, it flows out again through the commutator into the other carbon brush.

As soon as electricity flows through the armature coils, it makes the armature into a magnet. The north pole of the armature is attracted by the south pole of the stator. The south pole of the armature is also attracted by the north pole of the stator. This makes the armature turn. The shaft of the motor turns round as the armature turns.

When the armature turns to a certain point, it might be expected to stop. Its north pole must reach a point as close as it can reach to the south pole of the stator. But the armature is turning very quickly. It moves past that point, because of its momentum. Now the electric current passing through the armature changes direction. It does this because the commutator has turned as well. Different pieces of metal in the ring are in contact with the carbon brushes. The electricity in the coils of the armature flows in the other direction.

The north pole of the armature turns into a south pole. As soon as it does this it is pushed away from the south pole of the stator. Now it is the north pole that attracts it. So the armature keeps on turning. In most electric motors, there are several separate coils in the armature. It acts like a magnet with many different north and south poles. The poles change continually as the armature spins and makes the commutator change the direction of the current. The more separate coils there are, the more smoothly the motor turns.

Electric motors that use AC work in a different way. In one kind, the alternating current is passed around coils in the stator. The result is a moving magnetic field. When there is a moving magnetic field, it causes current to flow in wires nearby. This is called induction. Induction makes an electric current flow in the coils of the armature. This makes the coils behave like magnets. The moving magnetic field of the stator makes the coils of the armature spin. The armature turns the shaft of the motor. This kind of electric motor is called an induction motor.

Another type of electric motor that uses alternating current is called the synchronous motor. In this type the rotor spins at the same speed as the turning magnetic field of the stator. Electric clocks usually have synchronous motors. They have to have a constant speed of rotation. Synchronous motors are also used in other scientific instruments, such as telescopes, which must turn smoothly.

D.W./R.W.L.

The electric automobile (below) draws its electricity from a battery which it carries. Vehicles powered by electricity do not pollute the air with fumes, unlike some vehicles which burn certain types of gasoline or diesel oil.

ELECTROCARDIOGRAM (i lek′ trō kärd′ ē ə gram′) The electrocardiogram, abbreviated ECG or EKG, is a recording of the electrical activity of the heart muscle. The ECG from the normal heart shows impulses of a certain size and shape. When the heart muscle is not working properly because of disease or some other disorder, the ECG is changed. Such changes aid the doctor in making a diagnosis of why the heart is not beating normally.

The ECG is made by a machine called the electrocardiograph. This instrument has wires with electrodes at the ends. The electrodes are attached to the skin of the person. They pick up tiny changes in electrical activity from four points around the heart. These electrical impulses are sent through a voltage amplifier to make a recording by moving a pen across a strip of moving paper. Certain machines record the electrical activity on magnetic tape that can be played back for viewing on an oscilloscope. P.G.C./J.J.F.

ELECTROCHEMISTRY (i lek′ trō kem′ ə strē) Electrochemistry is the branch of chemistry that deals with the chemical effects of electricity on substances. It also deals with the production of electricity in chemical reactions. These subjects are most easily studied in solutions of electrolytes. Electrolytes are substances that, when dissolved or melted, conduct electricity.

Electrochemistry involves the study of ions in gases, solutions, molten substances, and some crystals. The ions (atoms carrying an electrical charge) make it possible for electric currents to pass through these substances.

Another subject of electrochemistry is the conversion of chemical energy to electricity. This occurs in dry cells used in flashlights and in automobile batteries. (*See* BATTERY; CELL, ELECTRICAL.)

In electrolysis, electrical energy is used to produce chemical changes. Hydrogen, chlorine, and caustic soda are produced commercially by the electrolysis of salt water. Electrolysis is used in electroplating and in obtaining many metals from their ores.

Electrochemistry is also concerned with the study of corrosion. By studying corrosion processes, scientists can find ways to protect metals. In biochemistry, electrophoresis is used to analyze and separate proteins.

The study of electrochemistry is very important in science and industry because it explains the electrical effects and reactions that occur. J.J.A./A.D.

ELECTRODE (i lek′ trōd′) An electrode is the terminal of any electric source. In other words, an electrode is an electrical conductor by which an electric current enters or leaves a medium. (*See* CONDUCTION OF ELECTRICITY.) For example, in electrolysis, a current enters and leaves a solution by way of two electrodes, the anode and cathode. The anode is connected to the positive terminal of the electricity supply. The cathode is connected to the negative terminal of the supply. In an

In this electric furnace (below) the arc between two graphite electrodes provides the heat to melt iron, bronze, steel, and other metals and alloys. Another important use of electrodes is in electrolysis.

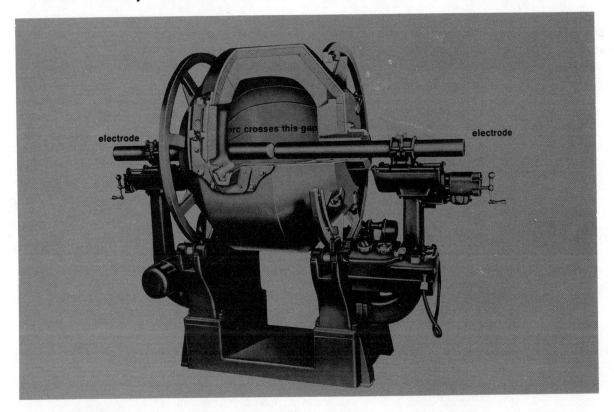
electrode · arc crosses this gap · electrode

electric cell, the positive terminal is called the anode. The negative terminal is called the cathode. (*See* CELL, ELECTRICAL.) Electrons can flow from the cathode, through a circuit, to the anode. Some vacuum tubes, besides having a cathode and anode, have other electrodes called grids. Ordinary transistors have three electrodes called the emitter, base, and collector. *See also* ARC, ELECTRIC; CURRENT, ELECTRIC; FARADAY, MICHAEL.

J.J.A./J.T.

ELECTROENCEPHALOGRAPH (i lek′ trō in sef′ ə lə graf′) The electroencephalograph is an instrument that measures and records electrical impulses from nerve cells in the brain. These recordings of the electrical activity of the brain, called electroencephalograms (abbreviated EEG) show the state of this activity. Normal EEG's have a frequency of 10 to 12 Hz. These are called alpha waves. Normal alpha waves occur when a person is awake and relaxed. When the person concentrates, the alpha waves decrease, giving way to smaller, faster waves.

During sleep, or when a person is unconscious, brain waves become very slow. Brain waves originate from the nerve cells in the brain. If these nerve cells become damaged by a head injury, by an infection in the brain, or by lack of oxygen, the EEG will be changed. Doctors have studied the EEG, and have learned how to diagnose epilepsy and to locate brain tumors.

P.G.C./J.J.F.